Freaky Future

Freaky Future

OVER 1,500 FACTS AND PREDICTIONS FOR TOMORROW'S WORLD

MARK FRARY

METRO BOOKS
NEW YORK

© 2010 Elwin Street Productions

This 2010 edition published by Metro Books,
by arrangement with Elwin Street Limited.

Designer: James Lawrence

See page 128 for picture credits

Conceived and produced by
Elwin Street Limited
144 Liverpool Road
London N1 1LA
www.elwinstreet.com

Metro Books
122 Fifth Avenue
New York, NY 10011

ISBN- 978-1-4351-2258-1

Printed and bound in China

1 3 5 7 9 10 8 6 4 2

Contents

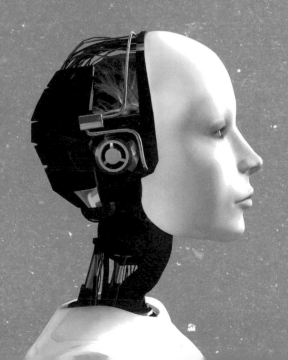

LIFE
BUT NOT AS
WE KNOW IT

Sci-fi predictions of life today

It is the job of the science fiction writer to predict how we would live in the future. Most wisely choose to set their novels far into the future so that by the time that date comes round, the author is long gone and cannot be accused of inaccuracy.

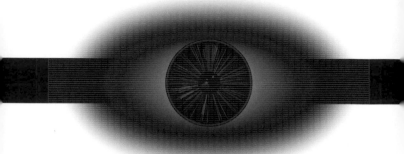

ABOVE In the future could all of our actions be monitored, like in George Orwell's *1984*?

1984: *George Orwell's 1949 novel predicted a future of a world wracked by war, where people's thoughts and actions are constantly monitored in their homes and in public by the ever present Big Brother – an idea that has passed into the English language. It also predicted the concept of political spin, where everything the populace hears or sees has been modified to mirror the views of the ruling party.*

Space 1999: At the heart of the Space 1999 conception of the future is a permanent base on the moon and the use of our nearest neighbor as a nuclear waste dumping ground, both of which seem to be a long way off happening in the current environment. The series also predicted that the universe was full of alien civilizations waiting to be discovered.

2001: A Space Odyssey: This film and screenplay by Arthur C. Clarke and Stanley Kubrick made many predictions for the future, including another permanently manned base on the moon, a space station orbiting Earth with its own Hilton hotel, the technology to mount a Jupiter space mission, and artificial intelligence in the form of Hal 9000.

Smart houses

The smart house idea has long been a staple of science fiction but in many ways has actually been reality for a number of years.

Universal control

The idea of being able to control everything in your house – closing the curtains, turning the heating down, turning on the TV, checking the fridge for food that's out of date – from a single remote control is a compelling one. This is why a number of wiring and communications systems, both wired and wireless, have been developed to do all of these things, including X10, OpenWebNet, and HomePlug.

Retro-fitting existing homes to make them smarter is likely to become more popular in the future and, given the challenge of rewiring, the technology to do so is likely to be wireless, using wi-fi and broadband mobile.

Smart toasters

To make homes smart, the things inside them need to become smarter too. Expect all new household appliances to come with computer chips and an internet connection in the future. This way, you'll be able to turn anything on and off from wherever you are in the world and monitor everything that goes in your home.

Your house may even be able to send you messages to keep you updated. Technology such as motion and door sensors could tell you any information you want to know about what's going on at home, like who's arrived home and when.

Eco-house of the future

One of the ways we can hope to turn the tide of climate change for the future is to buy into the concept of an eco-house. Building houses is a costly business both in terms of money and environmental impact, and we will need to build our homes of the future using cheaper materials that are also less damaging to the environment.

Much of today's housing is very wasteful. We keep houses too warm, flicking on the central heating instead of slipping on a sweater. In many "advanced" countries, houses are getting bigger and bigger, and are consuming more and more power. All of this will have to change if we are to be truly green.

Changing technology

Many technologies that can help us make this change do exist today – such as solar panels and breeze chimneys – and there are ways to develop these existing technologies to increase efficiency. There are also other technologies on the horizon, for example, one particular area for the future is for using building materials that are grown as opposed to ones that are manufactured, such as TreeNovation (see chart opposite). However, the reality is that these are unlikely to become mainstream.

So what can we expect to see? The chart on the opposite page offers some suggestions.

FACT

Earth sheltering is a sustainable architecture technique in which at least one side of a building is made of some form of earth (a grass roof or clay walls), such as the School of Art, Media, and Design in Singapore, which has a roof made completely of grass.

Building technology	Development	Why
Solar panels	Excitonic solar panels	Silicon-based solar panels are reaching the limits of their efficiency. Excitonic panels which use other materials and nano-technology promise to convert more of the sun's power into electricity.
Bricks	Fly ash bricks	Power stations create vast amounts of fly ash as waste. It can be made into bricks using a technique that requires no heating in a kiln and can be slotted together with less mortar.
PVC	Replacement with other materials	PVC is used widely in building but its production can be highly polluting, so it may be replaced with more environmentally friendly materials, such as fiber board and aluminum.
Wood	TreeNovation	A technique to grow fig tree roots into specific shapes, such as walls. The roots are amazingly strong and get stronger over time. After five years, they are as strong as steel construct while after ten years, they are stronger than concrete. The trees act as carbon dioxide sinks while growing.
Glass	Smart glass	This glass contains particles which can change the amount of heat and light passing through when a voltage is applied. It has the potential to help householders save money on heating and air conditioning.
Paint	Eco-paint	Traditional paint contains volatile organic compounds (VOCs). New "eco-paints" reduce or remove these VOCs.

Inside the future home

If you believed all you read in the 1950s, you would now expect to be living in homes populated by robots, delegating all the household tasks to them. So what happened?

Domestic robots

The Roomba: *Probably the most successful domestic robot in production, the Roomba is a round robot that trundles around your house and vacuums the floor wherever it goes, all without human intervention (well, sort of).*

Automower: *Swedish manufacturer, Husqvarna, have created a similar bot to Roomba that, instead of cleaning your carpets, mows your lawn. Once programmed, you should never have to touch it again. It goes about its daily business of grass-trimming, staying clear of flowerbeds and paths. When it's finished, it goes back to its recharging dock.*

Future developments

Robots are being developed all the time. From those that talk and interact with the old and infirm, offering company to those that need it, to robo-pets that do the same things a normal pet does (almost) without the need to feed and clean up after them. Although the visions of robot-run homes from the 50s haven't been reached just yet, we can be assured they will one day.

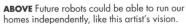

ABOVE Future robots could be able to run our homes independently, like this artist's vision.

Future hygiene

Personal hygiene has changed very little over recent years apart from the invention of automatic sensors for flushing toilets and turning on taps and hand dryers in public toilets.

Sci-fi soap

Soap, for instance, is very similar today to when it was first realized that it could be used for cleaning. It's unlikely to disappear any time soon but that doesn't mean that no one is looking at alternatives.

Where we may see a development is in personalized cleaning lotions. Imagine using a soap or other cleaning product that has been developed to match your skin and DNA perfectly, that will not only make you cleaner but also reduce wrinkles and help improve your overall health.

Sonic showers

Anyone who has ever stood in front of a loudspeaker at a concert or nightclub will realize the pressure that sound can exerts so there is a physical principle at work here.

Two systems are already in wide use for cleaning using sound – one where an object is placed in a bath of solution and ultrasound passed through the liquid. The ultrasound creates bubbles in the liquid which collapse forcefully, removing contaminants from the object's surface. However, using this system for people would be problematic since water is not a very good liquid to use and it is little different from taking a bath.

Another system is used for cleaning boilers and pipes. Low frequency sound waves are passed through the gas in the system and the fluctuations loosen any dust or ash particles stuck to the walls – but standing in a stream of gas is unlikely to appeal to people either.

Future slumbers

We spend two thirds or our lives in bed replenishing our energy stores. Science fiction has often imagined ways this basic human need can be altered for the benefit of all.

Hybernation

Hasan Alam, a surgeon at Massachusetts General Hospital, is researching an injectable solution that can rapidly reduce body temperature in people, putting them into a sort of hibernation. Alam has already shown that the technique works in pigs for periods of 20 minutes. The research is aimed at helping people survive the ambulance dash to hospital but others will no doubt look to extend this into longer hibernations.

Beds of the future

The beds of the future will be nothing like those of today. They will still be comfortable and warm (hopefully) but they are likely to be packed full of sensors to monitor your vital signs and status. With such technology, various things could be possible: if it sensed that you were enduring back pain, it could turn on localized massage pads that work away gently while you sleep. If the pain is worse than can be treated with a good massage, it could inject you with the appropriate drug – not using a sharp needle but by the

FACT

Cryonic procedures are regularly featured in science fiction as a means of traveling long journeys in space or to transport a character from the past into the future. In reality, such procedures are not yet reversible and may only be performed on people who are already legally dead.

application of a skin patch. And all while you dream blissfully. Sensors could also monitor the ambient and your body temperature, adjusting the heating and cooling circuits that make up the bed to keep you just right. The technology for this all exists or is under development, so it could just be a matter of time before it is implemented in the bedroom.

ABOVE A vision of hibernation monitored in an enclosed bubble.

Magic mattresses

The future may see the whole concept of the material bed disappearing, to be replaced by a system that keeps you in a comfortable position using a combination of magnetic and anti-gravity levitation. Researchers have already levitated a frog using a scientific property of living cells known as diamagnetism. However, it requires enormously strong magentic fields, which are expensive to operate and may or may not prove harmful to human health.

Accelerated learning

People have long yearned for an easier way to learn. Trawling through books, committing things to memory, and learning new skills is time-consuming and difficult to master. The future could hold the key to a brighter, smarter you!

Sleep learning

Sleep learning, or hypnopedia, the ability to learn from hearing things while you are asleep, has long grabbed the imagination. Those eight hours seem very wasteful, but if you could only develop another skill simply by listening to a recorded listen-while-you-doze, how great that would be. Some studies suggest that repetitive messages played while you sleep over a series of successive nights may help you retain new information. The consensus appears to be that learning occurs during brief disruptions to the sleep pattern, which researchers term "microarousals."

Plug-in information

Scientists have speculated for years that one day we will be able to plug ourselves into the Internet and download information directly to our brain. To put such a notion into perspective, if you download information at the current maximum speeds offered by service providers, you'd digest the contents of a 500 word book in two tenths of a second!

Cyberpunk writer, William Gibson seems to be one of the first thinkers of such technology. His ideas inspired the 1999 film, *The Matrix*, where the characters download any necessary skills, such as martial arts or the ability to fly a helicopter, through a plug inserted into their brains.

Biochemist Peter Fromherz is a pioneer in the field and his experiments have shown that living cells and computer chips can communicate. Sadly, the likelihood of having a *Matrix*-style learning device anytime soon are slim.

High-rise living

According to the World Bank, the world's population stood at 6.7 billion in 2008, and it is currently doubling every 33 years. With the population likely to continue to increase, we all might have to start moving into more high-rise accommodation.

This is already common in places where land is at a premium, such as Hong Kong, Singapore, and Dubai, home to the 2,716 ft (828 m) Burj Khalifa, the highest building in the world. We can expect to see more and more of these massive towers sprouting up all around the globe.

Extreme high-rise

The sky also offers residential opportunities – we might choose to live in permanently anchored airships if the ground gets too crowded. If Earth is not hospitable, we could always look at an orbital space station, the moon, or another planet in the solar system (see chapter 5).

Under the sea

If high-rise isn't the answer, we could look elsewhere. The Jules Underwater Hotel in Key Largo, Florida, shows that underwater living is possible so perhaps we might colonize the 71 percent of the Earth's surface that is water.

Hotels of the future

Savvy hoteliers are teching up their properties in order to attract digital natives, people who know nothing of the pre-internet world. New York's Algonquin hotel offers e-readers to its guests; Chicago's Avenue Hotel has dedicated ultrafast T1 internet connections and iMacs in its rooms; Hotel 1000 in Seattle monitors rooms via infrared to check the temperature and are fitted out with 40-inch LCD TVs and VoIP phones.

What to expect in your hotel room

The hotel of the future is going to have to do more than just add nice gadgets. Future hotels will have to be environmentally friendly in both their design and running: they will need to use recycled building materials, have integrated solar power plants, and will be built on brownfield sites. No longer will they shine with wasteful light 24 hours a day but instead stay dark unless you really need to see what you are doing.

Future hotels will also need to be flexible. We may be able to check in at any time of day or night, via a robot concierge who can also offer you advice on the local area, and be able to stay for as few or as many hours as you wish.

FACT
Hotel "pods" are predicted to become a feature of the future hotel industry. These would be temporary, pre-fabricated structures that could be transported and set up anywhere in the world. With an eco-friendly emphasis on their design, these pods would remain in place for up to 15 years, and dismantled as demand drops for a destination.

The hotel would know all of your personal preferences in advance – as some hotels do today – but taken to the extreme. The temperature of your room, the type and number of pillows, what you want in your minibar, the music playing as you enter the room, and the movies on your in-room entertainment system will all be set according to your tastes before your arrival.

Where we might stay in the future

We already have a hotel under the sea but where else could future travelers be resting their heads?

Where	What to expect
The high mountains	Hotel planned for the Klein Matterhorn in Zermatt, Switzerland at a height of 13,000 feet (4,000 meters).
Moon	Any development of a permanent base on the moon is certain to be followed by a lunar hotel.
Inside a waterfall	Forget watching the roaring waters from the side, be inside them.
Comets	Fancy the biggest buzz? Stay at a pop-up hotel (with solar protection) on a dirty snowball as it whizzes past the Sun.
The deep blue sea	Underwater hotels? Been there, done that. But what about one at the foot of the Marianas trench, the deepest point in the Earth's oceans and seas?

Freakish food and drink

As the world's population soars, it could become necessary to adapt the way we eat food. Pills have long been the vision of sci-fi creators but what about steaks grown in a lab?

Meal pills

Many sci-fi authors envisioned a future where food pills would replace the need to eat large meals. Food pills are still firmly in the realms of fiction, although there are an increasing number of pill-based food supplements on the market, which vary in their efficacy – vitamin, garlic, and fish oil pills, for example.

To be able to survive, people need to ingest certain things that their bodies do not contain or cannot create themselves. These essential nutrients include certain types of fat, some amino acids, some key vitamins, and dietary minerals – chemicals such as calcium and magnesium.

Any successful food pill would need to contain all of these nutrients. Perhaps the key challenge is getting enough of these nutrients into a pill-sized package.

Frankenstein feasts

In another area of research, scientists are trying to grow artificial meat in laboratory test tubes. In 2002, Dr. Morris Benjaminson of Touro College in New York successfully demonstrated the ability to grow artificial fish fillets from goldfish cells. The idea behind the experiment was to help in the development of food for astronauts on long missions away from Earth.

In 2009, scientists at Eindhoven University used a similar method to grow artificial meat in the laboratory. The results were described as resembling "soggy pork," although no-one has yet tasted the results of the experiments.

Universal food machines

Creating a universal food machine is a long way off. It goes way beyond the idea of creating artificial fish and meat in the laboratory.

Making artificial food would involve recreating the exact combination of atomic particles that make up real food. We can already create new particles to order in the world's particle accelerators but the process is energy hungry and not very compact. Creating the exact combination of particles we need and re-forming them into, say, a steak may become possible one day but something that you put on your kitchen table is likely to be out of the question for the next few decades.

FACT

In 2008, People for the Ethical Treatment of Animals (PETA) offered $1,000,000 to the first person to create chicken meat from stem cells and have it ready for the shops by 2012.

Thirst for adventure

Consumers are getting more adventurous in what they will drink, as shown by the rise in popularity of juices such as pomegranate and cocktails that mix exotic berries with more common ingredients. In the future, we could see this trend continue as well as the incorporation of gadgets and gizmos to make drinking even more personal.

While today we may drink things that contain "healthy bacteria" it is easy to see how we could be convinced to buy drinks that improve our IQ, reduce our BMI, and even tinker with our DNA to "correct" our genetic problems.

Fizzy fun

As well as healthy drinks, we want fun drinks. Already drinks makers are looking at drinks that change color and ones where you can customize the amount of fizz they contain by twisting a dial on the front of the can.

Meal in a glass

Where next? How about drinks that change taste according to what you are eating? Rather than matching wines with food, the wine would match itself to your palate. Meal drinks that actually taste like lobster thermidor or spaghetti Bolognese and give you all the same nutrients could also be next.

RIGHT Could future refreshments be tailored to your own personal tastes with the touch of a fingerprint?

Smart clothing

Athletes of the future may not wear running clothes made with ordinary textiles but rather with smart fabrics.

Medi-suite

Researchers at the Textile and Fiber Technology arm of the CSIRO research institute in Australia have incorporated data-conducting polymers into cloth. The materials have been designed to withstand the rigors of a washing machine. The idea behind these smart fabrics is to use them to monitor the athlete's bodily vital signs, such as heart rate and lung capacity, while they are running, helping their coaches to tweak their training scheuldes. This could, of course, be developed to allow for the monitoring of vital signs in everyone, ensuring we are aware of our health.

Space suits

NASA has also looked at smart fabrics. A 2005 project by Professor Dava J. Newman for NASA's Institute for Advanced Concepts looked at bio-suits for astronauts. Unlike the spacesuits that are common today, the planned bio-suits included electrically-actuated artificial muscle fibers which could be used to improve the astronaut's strength and stamina. Rather than being pressurized, the suit – which acts like a second skin – would be kept intact by a technology called mechanical counterpressure.

FACT

A snowboard clothing firm has created a jacket that incorporates wiring to control an MP3 player. It includes all the usual player controls on a panel located on the arm, and a socket in an interior pocket for connecting the player.

Sci-fi's best robots

Science fiction has dreamed up more robots than science has been able to bring into reality. Here are some of the best. Could we be seeing some familiar robo faces in the future?

Evil Bill and Ted: *In the second of the Bill and Ted movies, Bogus Journey, starring a young pre-Matrix Keanu Reeves and Alex Preston, the evil Chuck De Nomolos sends android clones of Bill and Ted back in time, with a mission to kill the originals in order to destroy their future utopia. While we are not planning to develop self-robots, we could create clones of ourselves to harvest for body parts when ours go wrong.*

R2-D2: *The cool droid easily wins out over his sidekick C3PO as the robot of choice from the Star Wars series of movies. He's a technical whiz and is good in a fight despite a lack of obvious weapons. R2-D2 might one day become reality. The US is spending heavily on military drones and an R2-D2 clone would be a logical avenue for development.*

FACT
The term "droid" was first coined by George Lucas in his *Star Wars* sagas. Today, any use of the word commercially must give Lucasfilm as a credit. Presumably, in the future all our droids will have the Lucasfilm logo on them somewhere!

Marvin: *Everyone always imagines robots as keen, strong, super helpers. The paranoid android from The Hitchhiker's Guide to the Galaxy destroys that myth once and for all. A more depressed and depressing robot you have never met. If we are looking at a future of living with robots, adding a few into the mix with individual personalities, even if they're not quite perfect, might help the integration of the human and robot populations.*

Robby the Robot: *Robby first appeared in the 1956 movie* Forbidden Planet, *which translated Shakespeare's* The Tempest *into a space setting. Robby was played by an actor in a mechanical suit, with a distinctive bell shaped glass dome containing electrical and mechanical workings for a head. Robby was a product of the 1950s and it is hard to see robot designers going for this look in their robots of tomorrow.*

Sonny: *The robot who dreams from the 2008, I-Robot, movie loosely based on Isaac Asimov's short stories. His virtually feature-free face is chilling and calming at the same time. The best thing is that you have to open up his skull to flick the switch that opens up the workings inside his chest. If robot-human relations are to run smoothly, we may need to make sure robot brains are capable of independent thought. Technology such as this is a long way off though.*

C3PO: *R2D2's golden chum seems only to be useful for one thing: understanding alien cultures and languages. When we explore the universe and find it to be teeming with alien life, a robot interpreter could be a good way to strike up diplomatic relationships.*

LEFT The *Star Wars* droids, C3PO and R2-D2.

Robot pets

They say that a dog is for life not just for Christmas. A robot dog could be for even longer than that. A robot pet that doesn't need feeding – except with electricity – and needs very little maintenance could well outlive you.

Like home helpers, robots have long been seen as a cheaper, easier, and much cleaner form of animal companion. Is there any comparison between these and the real thing?

Companionship

One future role for robotic dogs and other pets is as companions for the elderly. There is a strong body of research that shows how valuable real pets are as companions for the elderly. A robot dog might be able to provide that companionship too but also monitor their owner's health and remind them if they need to take medicine, have something to eat, or turn up the central heating in cold weather. Current technology could be used to make this a reality.

Guard dogs

Future robot pets may also work very well as supercharged guard dogs. They could use their robot sensors to detect if someone is moving around the house when they should not be, alerting the authorities to burglaries

RIGHT The AIBO toy dog can respond to physical and visual cues from its owner.

and shooting covert footage of the burglar using their onboard cameras. They might also be trained to attack and disarm the intruder, although some authorities may look dimly on that idea.

Robot pets: now and the future

There are a number of robot pets already available in stores or in development that might indicate what robotic friends we may have around our homes in the future:

Name	Description
AIBO	Dog. Most popular pet robot, selling tens of thousands.
Pleo	Dinosaur. Responds to sight, sound and stroking. Each develops its own personality over time.
Paro	Seal. Scientific project to see whether robot pets can be used in hospitals as a therapeutic aid.
iCat	Cat. Can alter its facial expressions and talk to its user. Designed to study human-robot interaction.
Robot goldfish	Goldfish. Some robot fish have already been made, including Jindong Liu's awesome robot carp.
Robot budgie	Budgie. We already have the annoying Squawkers McCaw robotic parrot. Miniaturization will make budgies and other cage birds a possibility.

Future power

Will we use solar, geothermal, wind, or fusion power in the world of tomorrow? The future as we forsee it will depend on mankind's ability to produce clean, efficient power.

Although the proven reserves of oil and gas have increased because of the discovery of new fields and the improvement of extraction techniques, we will eventually have to look at other energy sources in the future due to the problems of global warming.

Power source	Now	Future
Fusion	The Joint European Torus, currently the most advanced fusion experiment, produces substantially less power than it requires to operate.	The next big fusion experiment, ITER, will improve efficiency but a fully functioning fusion reactor is not expected until 2050 at the earliest.
Fission	Around 440 fission reactors in operation at present, generating around 370 GW of power.	Oregon State University is building a protoype reactor that uses helium instead of water as fuel and could be twice as efficient as any existing designs.
Solar power	Around 17 GW of solar photovoltaic power capacity globally at present, with Germany and Spain the leaders in the sector.	Researchers are looking at large panels for covering extensive areas, using organic materials instead of silicon in their design as well as flexible panels.

America's Energy Information Administration's World
Energy Demand and Economic Outlook, published in 2009,
predicts that energy production from liquids – largely oil –
will grow at the slowest rate, at an average of 0.9 percent a
year, although it will still remain the most important source
of energy in 2030.

The fastest growing source of energy will be renewables,
mainly hydroelectric and wind power, which are projected
to increase by 2.9 percent a year until 2030. So what types
of renewable energy are being developed?

Power source	Now	Future
Geothermal	Currently around 20 GW of geothermal capacity globally, mainly used for space-heating purposes.	Current research into hot dry rock geothermal, using boreholes drilled miles beneath the surface, could bring geothermal power to anyone.
Tidal	Small number of tidal projects in operation at present.	Many tidal projects in the pipeline, including a tidal barrage capable of generating 1320 MW around the islands west of Incheon in South Korea.
Wind	Around 60 GW of installed capacity at present. China is currently doubling its capacity every year.	Future innovations will focus on more offshore wind turbines, including floating installations as well as introducing "nodding" turbines that increase efficiency.

Garden gizmos and gadgets

The garden of the future is likely to be tended not by devoted human gardeners but by robots. We already have a model that can mow your lawn (see page 12), what other labor-saving devices might we see in our backyards?

The robo-horticulturalist

Something exciting for people who dream of robots tending their garden is being developed at MIT. The Distributed Robotics Garden is a project started in 2008 by Dr. Nikolaus Correll and Professor Daniela Rus. The garden is a series of pots and plants tended by a gardening robot.

The robot combines a mobile base, a robotic arm and gripper, a webcam, watering system, and the robot's brain – a notebook computer. Each plant pot is fitted with a humidity sensor and a wireless router. If the plant in the pot dries out, the sensor sends a signal to the robot asking for it to be watered.

Auto-harvester

The team is also experimenting with using the robot to harvest cherry tomatoes. The robot uses its webcam to distinguish between the dark red of a ripe tomato and its green leafy surroundings and then uses its robotic arm to lightly grasp and pick the tomato.

RIGHT The days of all-weather laboring in the garden could be over with new robot helpers.

TRANSPORT AND TRAVEL

Getting around in the future

From jetpacks to flying cars, teleportation to time travel, we all want exciting new modes of future transport, so what can we expect?

Awesome hoverboards

One of the most memorable things to come from the second *Back to the Future* film was the hoverboard, which appears to work on some sort of magnetic principle.

Magnets do offer one possibility. Magnetic levitation trains, for example, use the repulsive force between magnets on the train and in the tracks. However, it is clearly impractical to embed magnets underground throughout the world.

ABOVE Floating frogs in Nijmegen.

Floating frogs

Diamagnetism offers a possible solution. Virtually all materials exhibit some magnetic tendencies due to the electrons orbiting atoms. If you apply a magnetic field to a material, the object will be repelled.

However, it would have to be an extremely strong magnet. Researchers at Radboud University in Nijmegen, Netherlands levitated a frog in this way using a 16 tesla magnetic field.

Hover wobble

Stability is also an issue. Most magnetic systems would require some stabilizing mechanism so that the board would not flip over – not easy to add to a thin board.

Lastly, there is the issue of powering a board. Carrying large amounts of fuel or batteries is probably impractical so the power would need to come from an alternative source.

Super-fast elevators

The competition between the world's big cities to be home to the tallest building on the planet continues apace. Going hand in hand with that race for the skies is the glory of having the world's fastest elevators.

Race to the top

The world's fastest elevators are in the world's tallest building, the 1,669 ft (509 m) Taipei 101 tower in Taiwan. The pair of lifts, built by Japanese company Toshiba, can travel at 55 ft (17 m) per second. At this speed, designers have to think about the aerodynamics of the lift cabins. In order to reduce noise for occupants of both the lift and the building the cabins are shaped like bullets.

The space elevator

Forget tall buildings, the most exciting elevator project on the drawing board at the moment is one that will take you to space. The idea was conceived by sci-fi writer Arthur C. Clarke in his 1979 novel *The Fountains of Paradise*. In it, he came up with the idea of erecting a giant tether from the Earth's surface to a satellite in geostationary orbit. The advantage of this elevator is that things could be taken into orbit up the tether without the use of rockets.

FACT
Other Arthur C. Clarke–inspired ideas that scientists have been busily working on include powering rockets into space with nuclear energy, space probes landing on asteroids, and using a computer to back up your brain!

Techy trains

Maglev trains use magnetism to levitate above a track – hence the name. If you have ever tried to push two similar poles of a magnet together, you will realize that this has stability problems. Maglev trains typically use stabilization systems to monitor the position of the train constantly and make small changes to the strength of the magnets.

ABOVE A maglev train travels at 270 mph (431 kmph) in Shanghai, China.

Coming to a city near you!

Shanghai has the most advanced maglev system in the world: the Shanghai Transrapid between the city and Pudong International airport.

The possibility of other maglev links, between Abu Dhabi and Dubai in the Gulf and between Glasgow and London in the UK, is being explored. One of the most ambitious proposals is a 186 mile (300 km) line from Tokyo to Osaka via Nagoya, costing 5.1 trillion yen. Japanese rail firm JR Central says it hopes to get the line up and running by 2025.

Such a drag

One of the key factors stopping trains from going really fast is drag. Maglev gets around one part of this by not having the train in contact with any rails. However, as the trains get faster the challenges of aerodynamic drag begin to mount up. But what if there was a way to reduce its effects to virtually zero?

One way of doing this is to put a train inside a vacuum. There is a company that believes it can be done and at a cost of around $2 million per mile. Evacuated Tube Transport Technologies says its vacuum trains would be able to reach speeds of 4,000 mph (6,400 kmph), allowing people to travel from Washington to Beijing in just two hours. The company's system uses small, pressurized capsules which are magnetically levitated inside vacuum tubes. Passengers would access the capsule through an air lock.

A scale model has been built at Southwest Jiaotong University in China and some of the principles of the design, such as the magnetic levitation launch system, have been validated.

Underwater train travel

Other engineers believe the vacuum idea is viable too. Ernst Frankel, a retired professor of ocean engineering at MIT and Frank Davidson, who worked on studies for the Channel Tunnel, believe that buoyant tunnels a few hundred feet below the surface of the ocean could be a cost-effective way to cross the Atlantic between the US and Europe at high speed. Frankel told *Popular Science* magazine in 2004, "From an engineering point of view there are no serious stumbling blocks."

FACT

As early as 1910, American engineering student Robert Goddard designed a prototype of a maglev train, and also proposed sending it through a vacuum tunnel. His design proposals were only found after his death in 1945. His planned train would have traveled from Boston to New York in 12 minutes, at an average speed of 1,000 mph (1,609 kmph). However, it wasn't until 1969 that the first patent for a maglev train was issued.

Monorails in space

If you look at futuristic cities in comic strips and films from the 1930s to the 1950s, there is one thing that is sure to be present – a monorail.

Of course monorails have been a reality for some time in our cities. The first working passenger monorail started in Cheshunt, Hertfordshire, England, in the 1820s. More recently, the Indian city of Chennai (formerly Madras) was due to get the biggest monorail in the world – with almost 200 miles (320 km) of track – but the project has been shelved. The next step in popular imagination is monorails in space.

Even setting aside the fact that we aren't yet able to terraform any of the planets in our solar system (see chapter 5), the challenges involved in setting up monorails on another planet will be huge, not least the transportation of miles of steel track from Earth. Keeping the cars sealed against the vacuum of space will be equally difficult.

ABOVE An artist's vision of how a monorail on Mars might look.

Jumpin' jetpacks!

Science-fiction writers of the 1920s knew nothing of the jet engine – it was not invented by Sir Frank Whittle until 1930 – but that didn't stop them coming up with the concept of the jetpack, effectively a strap-on engine.

The first leap

The first true jetpack was tested by the German military toward the end of the Second World War. The *Himmelstürmer* (Heaven Stormer) was intended to allow infantry to hop over minefields and get behind enemy lines. The plan was to use two pulse jets, one on the back for moving forward and one on the chest for steering. Jetpack technology has not really moved on in leaps and bounds since then. Flight time is still severely limited, with most packs holding only enough fuel to keep a person in the air for about half a minute.

ABOVE The Martin jetpack.

It hasn't stopped the fascination with jetpacks. In 2009, Eric Scott from Denver broke the world speed record for a jetpack several times in one weekend. It now stands at a scary 68 mph (109 kmph). Scott also used a jetpack to cross the 1,500 ft (450 m) wide Royal Gorge in southern Colorado the previous year. His flight time of just 21 seconds is the current record for flight time.

A new dawn?

One of the most recent pieces of technology, the Martin Jetpack, is not technically a jetpack as it is powered by twin rotors, but looks set to extend flight time to minutes rather than seconds.

Hypersonic planes

With the fall of the Concorde many believe the age of supersonic flight has taken a backward step. However, scientists see a bright future for planes that can travel at several times the speed of sound.

Ramjets: *Jet engines that rely on turbines become inefficient as the speed of the plane increases, largely because of the increasing temperature of the turbine blades. As a result aviation engineers have looked at options that do not involve moving parts. Ramjets are used in planes that travel at supersonic speeds (faster than the speed of sound – known as Mach 1). Air enters the engine and is slowed down to subsonic speeds. Fuel is then injected into the air and combusted. The exhaust comes out of the rear of the engine, pushing the aircraft along. Ramjets work best between Mach 3 and Mach 5.*

ABOVE An artists concept of a Scramjet, an X-43A Hypersonic Experimental Vehicle.

Scramjets: *Scramjets are typically used in planes for reaching hypersonic speeds (Mach 5 and above). In planes fitted with scramjets the engines usually form an integral part of the aircraft. Air is channelled along the underside of the aircraft and into the engine inlet. As the air enters the engine it slows down but remains at supersonic speeds, unlike in a ramjet. The reduction in speed increases the pressure of the air before it is mixed with fuel and combusted. Scramjets can only start to operate at about Mach 4.5 and so other technologies are needed to reach this minimum speed. Some engines combine both ramjet and scramjet operation, switching between the two at the appropriate point. The theoretical maximum speed achievable by a scramjet is Mach 25.*

The future of flying machines...

Air travel is developing all the time. But what bigger, better, and faster planes could we be seeing soon?

Plane	Manufacturer	Type of plane	Proposed specification
Fifth generation fighter aircraft	Sukhoi/HAL	Fighter plane capable of supercruise	Length: 72 ft (22 m) Wingspan: 46.5 ft (14 m) Max speed: 1522+ mph (2450+ kmph) Engines: 2 x Saturn-Lyulka AL-41F turbofans
Mantis	BaE Systems	Autonomous unmanned aircraft system	Length: 32–45 ft (10–14 m) Wingspan: 65 ft (20 m) Max speed: 300 knots Engines: Turboprop
Pelican	Boeing	High-capacity cargo plane	Length: 400 ft (122 m) Wingspan: 498 ft (152 m) Payload: 1,400 tonnes Max range: 10,000 nautical miles (over water) Engines: Turboprops
Skylon	Reaction Engines Ltd	Satellite launch/ passenger services	Length: 269 ft (82 m) Wingspan: 82 ft (25 m) Payload: 12 tonnes Engines: SABRE hybrid air-breathing/rocket engines
Solar Impulse HB-SIA	Bertrand Piccard and André Borschberg	Ultra long-range solar-powered aircraft	Length: 71.68 ft (22 m) Wingspan: 208 feet (63 m) Max speed: 43 mph (70 kmph) Engines: Solar-powered electric engines

Personal planes

In the future, many of us will have our own planes, or at least that's what NASA thinks. The organization believes that 45 percent of all miles traveled in the future will be on board personal air vehicles (PAVs). These vehicles will travel at 150 to 200 mph (240 to 320 kmph), have a range of up to 800 miles (1,200 km) and operate from short runways, typically less than 400 ft (120 m) long. PAVs will also have simple controls, meaning anyone – not just qualified pilots – would be able to use them.

In 2007, NASA held a challenge in partnership with the Comparative Aircraft Flight Efficiency Foundation of Santa Rosa, California with prizes totalling $250,000 for companies to develop PAVs.

The big winner on the day was Vance Turner's Pipistrel Virus, an experimental aircraft made from carbon fiber, which demonstrated fuel efficiency of 29.8 mpg, achieved a top speed of 162 mph (260 kmph), and was able to take off in just 736 ft (225 m).

ABOVE A futuristic concept of the flying car that could be the final answer to avoiding traffic jams.

Subs and AquaJellies

As in the skies, unmanned submarines look set to become an important part of the submarine fleet, thanks to their ability to operate in hostile underwater environments.

Russian sub

The Yuri Dolgoruky is the first of the latest generation of Russian nuclear submarines and is set to be the workhorse of the Russian navy for years to come. This Boeri class submarine is 557 ft (170 m) long, 32 ft (10 m) in diameter, and can travel silently at a speed of more than 25 knots.

AquaJelly

As well as traditional submarine shapes, designers are looking to nature for inspiration for the undersea vessels of the future. German company Festo has built the AquaJelly, an artificial jellyfish that comprises an electric drive unit, tentacles for propulsion, and LEDs and a radio for communicating with its charging unit and other AquaJellies.

Stingray

Meanwhile, Evo Logics, also from Germany, have been looking at how manta rays swim. They have used their studies to develop a subsea glider which can be used for various underwater tasks including hydrographic profiling, mapping the sea floor, and search missions.

Crazy cars

Cars have been at the center of personal transport for over a hundred years, but what changes could we see in the future?

Sky cars

One of the bright hopes for future car transport was the Moller M400 Skycar, although some doubt whether even this will really get off the ground. The original concept was for a flying car that could take off and land vertically, achieve fuel efficency of 20 mpg and have a range of 750 miles (1,200 km), with a top speed of 350 mph (560 kmph). However, despite millions of dollars of investment in research and development over several years, the M400 has yet to reach full production and the single prototype has only been able to demonstrate short flights while attached to a tether.

Beyond the Segway

The media were abuzz in 2001 with speculation about something called Project Ginger, led by inventor Dean Kamen. When unveiled, it was revealed to be the Segway personal transporter. At present the vision of millions of people commuting on Segways has not yet appeared.

The company's latest concept is called Project PUMA (Personal Urban Mobility & Accessibility), a joint venture with General Motors. The PUMA, (like a Segway for two with a roof for city transport), is set to have a top speed of 35 mph (56 kmph) and have a range of 35 miles (56 km) for every eight hours of charging.

RIGHT A Segway in action.

Supersonic cars

Being the first to break the sound barrier in a car, like being the first athlete to run a mile in under four minutes, is something that can only be achieved once. The sound barrier was first broken by a car known as Thrust SSC – the SSC stands for supersonic car – on 13 October 1997. It was driven by Andy Green in the Black Rock Desert, Nevada, and retains the world land speed record of 763.035 mph (1,227.986 kmph) today.

1,000 mph car!

Although the sound barrier has now been broken, thrill seekers do not want to stop there. A team including Green and led by former record holder Richard Noble is looking to build a car called Bloodhound SSC which aims to smash the 1,000 mph (1,609 kmph) barrier. Australia's Silver Bullet rocket car is aiming for a similarly high speed.

The most ambitious project is a vehicle called Imagine LSRV, currently being built in California. The team behind the vehicle, lead by Waldo E. Stakes, believes that the car will be able to reach speeds of Mach 2 or even Mach 3, close to the top speed of some of the fastest planes ever built.

FACT

Each year London's Royal College of Art presents a number of concept cars as part of its Master of Arts degree show. Hong K. Yeo's Volkswagen Concerto is one: a car that can be assembled from standard components in the same way as Lego bricks. He envisages people buying one car in their lives, plugging in extra seats if they have children and removing seats if they get divorced.

Future fuels

What fuel will future vehicles run on? It seems inevitable that today's reliance on fossil fuels must come to an end in order to save our planet and to provide an alternative if these sources eventually run out. There are a number of possible alternatives:

Fuels	Source	Benefits	Disadvantages
Bioethanol	Sugars from crops, such as corn, maize, and sorghum.	Absorbs CO_2 during cultivation, can be blended with existing petrol/gasoline.	Large amount of land required to grow could lead to deforestation, poor fuel economy.
Hydrogen	Extraction from natural gas and other fossil fuels, electrolysis of water.	No carbon emissions, non-polluting during use.	Costly to produce, carbon emissions relating to extraction from gas.
Nuclear power	Radioactive decay of fissile elements, such as uranium.	Cheap production if you use existing power stations to generate power for electric cars.	Disposal of radioactive waste, investment in new electric cars.
Solar power	The Sun.	Sustainable, can be used in remote areas, low cost after initial investment.	Not ideal for cloudy locations, require lots of space for efficient working.
Wind	The wind.	Renewable, non-polluting.	Unreliable.

Lightspeed!

There have been regular claims by scientists that they have discovered phenomena that involve faster-than-light travel.

Jumping photons

One of the most recent claims was by Günter Nimtz and Dr. Alfons Stahlhofen at the University of Cologne. They had built an experiment involving microwaves and two large prisms sandwiched together to make a cube. The scientists passed microwave photons into the prisms and observed where and when the photons emerged. The scientists then gradually moved the two prisms apart. Normally you would expect the microwaves to be totally reflected within the first prism but an effect called quantum tunnelling allows the photons to "jump" the gap between the two prisms.

Arriving before you leave

Nimtz and Stahlhofen claimed that the photons that were detected reflected within the first prism and those that tunnelled to the second arrived at exactly the same time, no matter how wide the gap was between the two prisms. They argued that this showed that the photos were traveling faster than light as they jumped between the two prisms. Other scientists have cast doubt on the research, arguing that Nimtz and Stahlhofen have not measured the time of arrival of the photons in the right way.

The wonder of Warp

Warp drives, the engines from *Star Trek*, which work by changing the shape of the space around a ship so that distant points are brought close together – are considered mathematically possible, but a viable mechanism for their operation has yet to be invented.

Teleportation travel

The word "teleportation" was coined by Charles Fort, the founder of the bizarre happenings newspaper *Fortean Times* in 1931. It comes from the Greek *tele-* meaning "far" and the French verb *porter*, meaning to "carry."

Teleportation, as widely outlined in science-fiction books and films, requires you to wear or step inside some device. This device somehow transfers you, either instantaneously or after a short delay, to a distant location.

Descriptions of teleportation usually involve some mention of the "space-time continuum" and bending it, making holes in it or stepping outside it briefly to achieve a hop from one place to another without actually traveling.

Why we'll need it

If humans and their space vehicles really are limited to a maximum speed of 186,411 miles (300,000 km) per second then it is going to take us way too long to reach anywhere interesting. The nearest star other than the Sun, Proxima Centauri, is 4.22 light years away. Going there and back, even if we could travel at near the speed of light, is going to take at least eight and a half years.

The problem with teleportation

How do you decide where the person ends and the air surrounding them begins? What happens when you remove the person from their current location? Presumably the air surrounding them would collapse into the resultant vacuum, possibly damaging the teleportation device itself. At the other end, what happens to everything that exists in the space your person is going to? Does it get destroyed or do you have to do it inside a vacuum? There are many questions and problems that would need to be addressed in the development of this technology.

Wonderful wormholes

Have you ever thought what spacetime might look like?
Many cosmologists and writers use the analogy of a rubber
sheet. Large celestial objects, such as stars, can be
represented by a heavy object, such as a watermelon,
placed on the sheet. The bending of the sheet gives an idea
of how the heavy object warps spacetime, which we
experience as gravity.

Shortcuts through space

Now imagine that our rubber sheet has been folded into a
C-shape and that we put a burning hot cannonball on it.
The cannonball melts the rubber sheet and creates a tunnel
between the top and bottom of the C – this is what scientists
speculate a wormhole might be like. Now instead of
traveling around the bend of the C, we can travel through
the tunnel, cutting the distance we travel dramatically.

Do they exist?

There is no observational evidence for wormholes although
the equations of general relativity say they could possibly
exist. If they do exist, scientists believe they might be
available for interstellar travel. Caltech's Kip Thorne and
Michael Morris outlined how this could work in their paper
"Wormholes in Spacetime and Their Use for Interstellar
Travel." However, the two scientists needed to invoke weird
forms of matter to make the equations work.

ABOVE The USS *Enterprise*, from *Star Trek*.

The science of *Star Trek*

Science fiction is usually the starting point for most futuristic forethought. *Star Trek*, probably the most popular sci-fi brand in existence, contains some amazing technology but how realistic is it?

The tricorder: *In the series and films, Dr "Bones" McCoy waved a small box over patients and it could instantly say what was wrong with them. Bizarrely, despite this advance in technology, there was rarely anything Bones could do for them.*

Japanese robot manufacturer Tmsuk has perhaps got closest to this in reality. It developed its pre-hospital care robot for the Aichi Expo 2005. Anyone feeling unwell sits in it and it automatically takes readings of vital signs such as pulse rate, blood pressure, and heart beat rate.

The phaser: *The phaser, a contraction of photon maser, is one of the standard weapons in the Star Trek armory. It can stun, kill, or vaporize people and objects using a beam of fictitious but scientific-sounding* nadion particles. Phasers come in various shapes and sizes, from personal handheld weapons to starship-mounted cannons.

The closest we have to these weapons today are lasers. One of the most powerful lasers is the Linac Coherent Light Source, a powerful X-ray laser which opened at SLAC in April 2009.

The tractor beam: *In Star Trek, tractor beams are used to pull objects, particularly spaceships, without being physically connected to them. They are said to work using the graviton, the hypothetical particles that mediate the force of gravity.*

Gravitons are unlikely to ever be observed in reality because of the huge scale of the detector required to feel their influence but there is already indirect evidence of gravitational waves.

Scientists at St Andrews University in Scotland have also used twisted lasers beams to manipulate tiny objects. It may be some time until we can do the same with spaceships.

Warp drives: *The USS Enterprise managed to achieve its five-year (ongoing) mission through the use of the warp drive, a means of traveling faster than light. It relies on the use of warp fields to form a protective bubble around the starship which warps the spacetime continuum. Warp engines are powered by a mixture of matter and anti-matter with the help of dilithium crystals.*

This is still in the realms of science fiction, although we have created small amounts of anti-matter at laboratories such as CERN and Fermilab.

FACT

Einstein's special theory of relativity puts a limit on how fast something can travel – that limit is the speed of light. Yet some scientists have theorized that the speed of light is both an upper and a lower threshold. It is an upper limit for anything that is traveling slower than light (tardyons) and a lower limit for anything that is traveling faster than light (tachyons). These tachyons can never be slowed down to below the speed of light if Einstein's equations are to be believed. Scientists have never observed tachyons.

The time machine

Was the science fiction writer H. G. Wells a time traveler? It's interesting to speculate that the man who wrote *The Time Machine* is actually from the future and he has traveled back to the Victorian era to write about it. Some have pointed to his predictions of world wars to support their claims.

The time travel test

In 1975, Einstein's theory of time-dilation was tested by American physicist Carrol Alley. She synchronized two atomic clocks and put one on an airplane. Back on the ground, she compared the two. The jet-board clock was microseconds behind the control, suggesting time had slowed fractionally with the speed of the plane. These ideas were revisited by astrophysicist Richard Gott in 1991. He concluded that closed timelike curves were theoretically possible, and could in the future be used as the basis for travel to the past.

Could it ever happen?

Ronald Mallet at the University of Connecticut theorized in 2001 that the gravitational field produced by a laser beam could be manipulated to allow time travel. Physicists have long suggested that wormholes might allow instant travel across time as well as space. However, physicist Stephen Hawking believes the laws of physics "conspire to prevent time travel, on a macroscopic scale," and the scientific evidence to refute this has yet to be discovered.

GADGETS
AND
GEEKERY

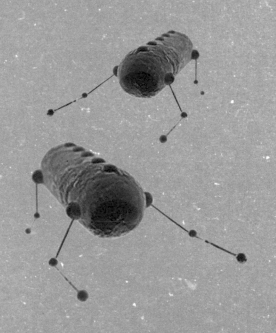

Gizmos and gadgets

What are the gadgets and computer technologies that will shape the future? In this chapter, we look at some of the latest technology being worked on in universities and corporate R&D labs to see what cool gadgets we can look forward to.

Virtual reality

Cinematographer Morton Heilig was one of the pioneers of virtual reality. In 1962, he built a device known as the Sensorama, which offered a virtual reality motorbike ride around Brooklyn. The user sat on a stool in front of the machine with their head enclosed by screens on which film from different cameras were projected. The stool could move too, giving the impression of bumps on the road surface. It was not a commercial success but it paved the way for the concept of virtual reality in the future.

Army VR

Arcade game maker Atari brought virtual reality to the masses with the release of Battlezone in 1980. This tank battle simulator used wireframe graphics to display a

LEFT US Navy personnel using a virtual reality parachute trainer, one of the many possible uses for VR as the technology develops.

landscape dotted with obstacles, tanks, and simplified mountains on the distant horizon. For arcade gamers brought up on Pong and Space Invaders, the 3D effects were mind-blowing and the game became incredibly popular as a result. The game was considered so realistic that the US Army asked Atari to produce a version called the Bradley Trainer, which was used to train soldiers using the Bradley Fighting Vehicle.

A virtual education

Virtual reality doesn't just have applications in games and entertainment, there is also great potential in a range of educational uses:

Teaching children to write: *The University of Buffalo is working on a project with the National Science Foundation, which uses a pen device and force feedback to help students learn to write.*

Digital heritage: *University College London's Center in Virtual Environments, Imaging, and Visualization is carrying out research on how to use VR to create 3D immersive versions of buildings, which are immune from the ravages of time, unlike the brick and mortar versions.*

Coping with autism: *The Oxford Autism Research Group is studying how VR environments can be used to teach children with autistic spectrum disorder how to relate effectively with their peers and also on crossing the road safely.*

Construction: *Austria's Institute of Software Technology and Interactive Systems is using infrared tracking of static and moving objects to look at how VR could be used to control tunnelling and various other pieces of construction equipment.*

Engineering simulation: *The Virtual Reality Applications Center at Iowa State University is developing virtual reality power stations as a tool to improve their thermal operation.*

The future of touch

Haptics is the study of touch and is a hot area of research. One cool example of haptic technology is the data glove, such as the CyberGlove II by CyberGlove Systems. Data gloves are lightweight gloves which incorporate sensors that can accurately track the position of your fingers and thumbs as well as whether your palm is arched and your wrist flexed.

Virtual hug

Philips Research in the Netherlands is working on what it calls an Emotions Jacket. This tight-fitting jacket contains actuators – a little like the vibrator motors in a mobile phone – which can be activated in response to what is happening on a television screen. The company says it can be used to deliver a much more immersive experience of watching a movie – if a couple cuddle on screen, you would be able to feel the cuddle yourself.

Long reach

Meanwhile, Hiroaki Yano and colleagues at the University of Tsukuba in Japan have developed a haptics device that allows users to "feel" objects that are beyond reach. It uses a laser range finder to work out the distance to the object and an actuator to recreate the small changes in distance presented by the surface of the object.

Seeing is believing

Although virtual reality has come a long way, few people believe that what they are witnessing is real. In a research project examining the stimuli that cause people to believe or disbelieve what they are seeing, researchers created a virtual reality bar, which subjects "entered." While they were in the bar, a virtual fire started and researchers noted that many of the subjects fled the virtual environment in panic.

Top five futuristic controllers

The introduction of the Wiimote in 2005 for the Nintendo console saw home games controllers enter a new era. What does the near future hold?

1. **Cywee:** *A wireless game controller that combines 3D motion sensing and a design that lets you twist it into different configurations, including a gun mode and a steering wheel mode.*

2. **Emotiv Epoc headset:** *Uses 14 sensors arranged around the head to detect electrical signals in the brain, which can be used to control movement and other actions inside video games.*

3. **Iron Will Innovations Peregrine glove:** *This glove contains 18 touch sensors and three activation pads. You control the game by touching your thumb and fingers together. The various touch combinations give access to 30 user-definable game actions.*

4. **PlayStation Motion Controller (or Sony Wand):** *A controller due for launch in 2010 which features a glowing orb at one end, containing LEDs. The position of the orb is tracked by the PlayStation Eye webcam and that of the rest of the wand by internal inertial sensors.*

5. **Project Natal:** *Microsoft's controller-free controller for the Xbox, due for launch in late 2010. It consists of a camera, depth sensor, and microphones, and it should allow gamers to play using just facial recognition, limb gestures, and full body movement.*

RIGHT Virtual reality software and hardware development, with program engineer wearing virtual reality display hood

Extreme entertainment systems

Entertainment in the future is likely to be an immersive affair. At the moment, when we listen to a music track, most of us just enjoy an audio experience, the changing pressure and frequency of sound waves on our ear drums.

The I-Helmet

If we look ten years ahead, it may be that the latest version of the iPod will come with a virtual reality helmet. When you buy an enhanced music track, you also get access to 3D footage of the recording of the track, enabling you to feel as though you were in the studio when it was being made.

Moviemaker

A possible additional feature for future movie releases may be an option for you to be the director. All of the scenes will be provided as part of the download and you will be able to assemble them as you wish. All of your followers and friends on social networks will vote on your directorial efforts.

Holograms

Star Trek: The Next Generation (1987–1994) popularized the holodeck, a virtual reality facility that allowed users to re-create and experience anything they wanted. While elements of the holodeck are possible today, others still have a long way to go. While 2D holograms exist, for example, 3D holograms don't, and the force fields required to make a hologram feel real are still science fiction. Perhaps the closest thing to a holodeck today is immersive game technology developed at the Helsinki University of Technology in Finland. The researchers developed a game called *Kick Ass Kung Fu* that lets players fight onscreen enemies using real kicks, punches, or acrobatic fighting moves, as well as real props such as axes or swords.

Eyephones

Imagine walking down a street in a foreign city for the first time and instantly being able to tell where the nearest cash machine is, what visitors to that restaurant you just passed thought of it, and a walking route through the city? We are on the verge of just that thanks to two types of technology – retinal imaging and augmented reality (AR).

Retinal imaging

This is the idea of actively projecting images onto the retina of the eye itself rather than watching something on a screen. The most exciting concept for using retinal imaging are eyephones, a pair of spectacles with an integrated retinal image projector.

Eyephones are not in the realm of science fiction. In 2008, printer company Brother announced it had developed a prototype wearable retinal imaging display module that attached to a pair of spectacles. The device allowed a small image with a resolution of 800x600 to be projected onto the retina using low-intensity light which could be updated 60 times a second. They could be used for reading confidential material in public or perhaps for engineers carrying out maintenance work, where the eyephone could display a schematic diagram of the equipment being worked on over the top of the equipment itself.

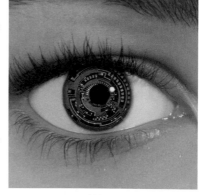

ABOVE Images could be projected directly onto retinas or spectacles for easy-access information.

Augmented reality

The eyephone concept is related to the idea of augmented reality (AR), which has become a hot issue thanks to the success of smartphones and Apple's iPhone in particular.

AR applications take the image from a smartphone's camera and overlay additional information over the top. AR is being used to allow smartphone users to see details of nearby shops, hotels, and other points of interest. With some applications you can point the phone's camera at a building of interest and, using GPS and other location data, pull information on the building from the web.

Communication, sci-fi-style

Space Cadet: *In this novel by Robert Heinlein from 1948 novel, the main character Matt Dodson has a phone that he carries in his pocket. That's an eerily prescient prediction.*

Star Trek (original series): *William Shatner and colleagues probably had the closest idea of what a future cell phone would look like with the communicator. Its flip-design has been mirrored in many real-life phones. Shame you can't use the real phones over sub-space frequencies though.*

Star Trek (2009): *The latest outing of the Enterprise shows the young James T. Kirk driving a red Corvette fitted with a futuristic Nokia touchscreen videophone.*

The Machine Stops: *This short sci-fi story by E M Forster was written in 1909. In it, one of the characters uses a handheld round disc to see and speak with their son on the other side of the Earth.*

2001: A Space Odyssey: *Arthur C. Clarke and Stanley Kubrick failed to predict the arrival of mobile phones but in the film Dr Heywood Floyd is shown wishing his daughter happy birthday by a videophone controlled by voice identification.*

Fantasy cell phones

As we have seen, science fiction has imagined some amazing communication devices over the years but it is possible that what we will actually see in a few years will amaze even these most imaginative of thinkers!

Top concepts

1. *Zyxio have developed a prototype phone controlled by breath – the strength of your exhalations governs how quickly you are able to scroll through phone menus.*

2. *Another funky phone came from TeleEpoch, which didn't have any buttons. Entering numbers is done through voice control and scrolling through menus using gestures – the phone contains accelerometers.*

3. *A company called SealShield unveiled a dishwasher-proof mobile phone – you suspect that the forgetful will not be the phone's primary market but rather the clumsy who spill their cups of coffee.*

4. *The recently unveiled Touch Wood phone from NTT DoCoMo is built using surplus wood from trees culled during thinning operations. This is a step in the right direction for managing the problem of disposing old mobile phones, particularly when many users get a new phone under their monthly contract every year, and a possible way to reduce the environmental impact in the future.*

FACT

According to a UN report in 2008, 60 percent of the world's population owned a cell phone. Even the poorest countries in Africa have seen a massive increase in users. It is not unreasonable to predict that everyone will own a cell phone within the next 50 years.

What next for portable computing?

The IBM 5100, which was launched in 1975, is regarded as the first ever portable computer. It had a built-in screen and tape drive, offered up to 64K of storage, and cost up to $20,000. It doesn't seem very portable by today's standards – it weighed 55 lbs (25 g) and was the size of a suitcase.

Good reads

E-readers are the next thing that are slowly gaining in popularity, with the launches of the Amazon Kindle and the Sony e-Reader. The early 2010 launch of Apple's iPad, sitting somewhere between the iPod Touch and a netbook looks set to see such devices jump into the mainstream. The iPad, with its intuitive gesture-based interface, will make reading books, as well as newspapers and magazines, much more like their paper-based predecessors.

Future Internet

Connecting to the Internet is a key feature of most portable computing and gadgets these days, and the Internet is evolving too. Social networking, blogging, wikis, and search engines are all part of what has become dubbed web 2.0, so what can we expect to develop next?

Many people think that web 3.0 will be what world wide web inventor Sir Tim Berners-Lee calls the semantic web. The semantic web is one where data is tagged so that other websites and applications can use it easily. For example, the figures from the annual accounts of a company would be tagged with what they mean, allowing the figures to be manipulated and compared with the figures from other companies quickly and easily. A semantic web would make mash-ups – where you take data from more than one source and display or use it in a new way – simple.

Most wanted gadgets

What kind of gadgets could technophiles be clamoring for in the future?

What	Why	When
Transparent screens	So you can see people coming if you are checking out something you shouldn't on your laptop.	MP3 players with transparent screens are expected this year. Prototype laptops were shown in 2010 but with no release date.
iPhone 3DS	Forget the 3GS version, we want the model you can use to watch *Avatar* and videophone your friends in glorious 3D.	2011. Purely conceptual at this stage but the success of *Avatar* and 3D screens in general mean this cannot be far off.
Galileo global navigation system	A European civilian-operated system with location accuracy to a few centimeters.	Satellite constellation should be operational by 2014.
Gigapixel handheld camera	We want to be able to zoom into photos in virtually infinite detail like in *Blade Runner*.	It took around seven years after digital cameras were launched to increase the average resolution by a factor of 10. At that same rate we should see a gigapixel handheld camera by around 2021.
Social networking implant	Rather than wasting time on Twitter and Facebook, this neural implant posts your current thoughts of all kinds to every social network everywhere instantaneously and communicates via next generation Bluetooth with nearby devices to find people with similar desires.	2025. Prof Kevin Warwick's Project Cyborg has already shown the feasibility of implants while social networking is second nature to many. However privacy concerns will see this as a delay to this implant's arrival.

Future watches

Those of us who grew up reading the comic book *Dick Tracy* are now close to being just like our hero, at least in terms of his choice of watch. Over the years, Tracy sported a number of different devices on his arm – a two-way wrist radio, then a wrist videophone, and finally a wrist computer.

Telling the time in style

In the past two or three years, true computers have made their way onto people's wrists, such as the WL series from Zypad, which run on Arm chips and can run Linux.

Watch maker Timex recently held a design competition to explore the future of time and watches in particular. The designs, submitted by watch lovers and professional design teams, were wide-ranging and innovative.

`1:01  00:02  00:03  00:04  00:05  00:`

Top three futuristic watches

1. **Time-aid:** *A watch including a small central video screen which can show a live feed from thousands of watches and clocks around the world, such as the face of Big Ben in London or the flower clock in Geneva's Jardin Anglais.*

2. **4037:** *A translucent, elastic wristband with the digital time integrated into it so the display can stretch and distort with the band. A gravity sensor continually shifts the numbers to the top for easy reading.*

3. **TX54:** *A translucent film that attaches to your fingernail showing the time in glowing colors.*

`:54  23:55  23:56  23:57  23:58  23:`

Supercomputers to come...

IBM has announced that its next supercomputer will be called Sequoia and it is expected to be ready in 2011 or 2012. It will use a whopping 1.6 million processors and the company claims it will be capable of performing 20 petaflops.

Designers will need to look at options other than silicon for the future, however, as it is likely that miniatutrization will reach a barrier. Chip designers are not worried: researchers at the Niels Bohr Institute at Copenhagen University predict that future supercomputers will use photon-transistors, which will use individual light photons to store binary digits and will help achieve greater speeds and degrees of miniaturization. Other teams are looking at processors made from biological materials and carbon nanotubes that would be able to allow designers to leap over this seemingly impenetrable barrier to greater computing power.

Current supercomputers

Computer	Manufacturer and system	Number of cores	Location	Performance
Jaguar	Cray XT5	224,162	Oak Ridge National Laboratory, Dept. of Energy, USA	1.75 petaflops
Roadrunner	IBM Blade Center QS22/ LS21 Cluster	122,400	DOE/NNSA/LANL, USA	1.04 petaflops
Kraken	Cray XT5	98,928	Nat. Institute for Computational Sciences/University of Tennessee, USA	832 teraflops
Jugens	IBM Blue Gene/P Solution	294,912	Forschungszentrum Juelich, Germany	825 teraflops

Nanotechnology

Nanotechnology is the science of matter on a scale of 1 to 100 nanometers (10^{-7} to 10^{-9} meters). It has become a hot topic thanks to miniaturization and in particular thanks to the insatiable appetite to pack as many transistors onto a computer processor as possible. It is all about creating chips, machines, and mechanisms on a truly tiny scale, the scale of molecules. However, nanotechnology offers challenges to chip designers and scientists because at these small scales, the normal rules of physics don't always apply.

There are many concerns about the safety of nanotechnology, for environmental and health reasons, as well as for potential security and privacy issues with advanced undetectable technology such as weaponry and surveillance.

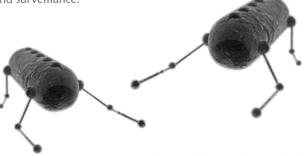

ABOVE Artist's concept of how nanobots may look.

FACT

"Gray goo," a term used by nanotechnology pioneer Eric Drexler in his 1986 book *Engines of Creation*, is the theory that nanotechnology could lead to the end of the world in the event of out-of-control self-replicating robots consuming all matter on Earth while building more of themselves.

Potential applications of nanotechnology

The potential applications of nanotechnology are limitless. However, some of the more obvious areas where it can be used are shown below.

Use	Description
Bone tissue repair	At Brown University in Rhode Island, scientists are working on a hydrogel made from nano-materials that can be used to help restore bone tissue damaged from cancer and osteoporosis.
Nanobots	Scientists and engineers are already building miniaturized robots for simple tasks. Future nano-sized bots might be able to search for and destroy cancerous cells in the human body, rebuild the ozone layer, and clean up environmental pollutants.
Novel materials	At the nano scale, materials start behaving differently than at larger scales. Carbon nanotubes, in particular, are lightweight but extremely strong and have applications in the aerospace and automotive industries.
Solar power	Researchers at Rensselaer Polytechnic in New York have developed a prototype solar panel that is highly efficient in absorbing the sunlight that falls on it by funneling light from different angles. One of the problems of existing solar technology is that they are inefficient because they work best when sunlight is falling directly on them.
Tumor imaging	A number of teams around the world are working on the application of quantum dots, semiconductors that are confined in three dimensions and emit high frequency light. These have been used instead of fluorescent dyes in the laboratory to image cancerous tumors.

Cloud computing

If the past two decades have been the age of the desktop, the next two, at least, will be the era of the cloud. This is the nebulous name given to the Internet when it is used to store data or run applications that were typically held on your desktop PC.

The advantage is that your data and software are not tied to a single computer – you can access them from anywhere with an Internet connection and, with the added processing speeds of all the computers on the cloud, you can do everything much more quickly.

Grid computing

Solving difficult problems – be they scientific or commercial – is often handled by computers. But what happens if your problem is so tough – trying to work out what happens when particles collide inside the Large Hadron Collider (LHC) for example – that the problem is too big for the computing resources of one organization?

Computer teamwork

The answer, increasingly, is to use grid computing and it looks set to become an increasingly common way of problem solving. The idea is that you link together computers in lots of different locations and get them to work together on a common problem.

Let's look again at the LHC. When it is fully working, it is expected to produce 37 terabytes of raw data every day. A grid of computers at host laboratory CERN and a grid of around 160 institutions around the world will crunch this data in the search for the so-called God particle, the Higgs boson.

BOINC network

The opening words on the website of the Berkeley Open Infrastructure for Network Computing (BOINC) is rather mind-blowing. It says "use the idle time on your computer to cure diseases, study global warming, discover pulsars."

BOINC uses the concept of grid computing where the resources of distributed computers on a network are pulled together to crunch a computing problem. In BOINC's case, it uses the unused processing power of desktop PCs owned by individuals and organizations around the world when the machine is on but is not being used by its owner.

At the time of writing, there were 587,897 computers in the BOINC network, with a performance of 4.7 petaflops (or 4.7 quadrillion mathematical calculations every second) – nearly three times as much as the most powerful supercomputer in the world.

There are various projects currently being run on the BOINC network, some of the biggest ongoing projects are detailed below.

Project	Purpose
Climateprediction.net	Running climate predictions for the planet up to 2080.
Folding@Home	Studying protein folding and molecular dynamics.
Milky Way@Home	Creating a detailed three-dimensional model of our own galaxy.
SETI@home	Searching for alien life.
World Community Grid	Studying protein folding to see how they might be used as drugs for combating diseases such as AIDS and cancer.

Artificial intelligence

The first computers that appeared in the 1940s and 1950s were seen as machines that could help in number crunching for tasks that were too time-consuming or repetitive for people to undertake themselves. However, as computers have become more powerful, there is now the thought that one day we may be able to create a new form of intelligence, one that is artificial rather than real.

Replica brains

The human brain contains around 100 billion neurons or brain cells, which control our functions and store our memories. These neurons are connected by synapses, of which there may be as many as 10,000 for each neuron, and which are used to send electrical and chemical signals.

Our knowledge of how neurons and synapses work exactly is incomplete but any attempt at building a replica brain would probably need to contain a similar number of elements and connections.

Mathematical model

The Blue Brain Project, based at the Ecole Polytechnique Fédérale de Lausanne in Switzerland, is one of the leading experiments trying to better understand the brain. Its main research focuses on creating a mathematical model of a part of the brain called the neo-cortex.

The project's direct Professor Henry Markram says that he believes that a model of how the brain truly works is technically and biologically feasible within the next 10 years, although there is little certainty about how much creating such a model would cost and whether anyone would actually fund it.

Self-replicating machines

Many nightmare scenarios in science fiction rely on the idea of self-replicating machines going out of control. As the name suggests, a self-replicating machine can make clones of itself using raw materials extracted from its environment.

Exploring the final frontier

The idea of such machines is particularly attractive in the field of space exploration. Here, the idea would be to create a spacecraft that would be able to explore the universe, landing on distant worlds and reporting back to Earth on what it found. Once on a distant planet, the spacecraft would create a clone of itself from local materials and then both would go on to explore and create further clones.

Fictional future?

This is not as futuristic as it seems. In 2008, researchers on the RepRap project at Britain's University of Bath used a 3D printer to create the parts necessary to build a clone of itself. That clone printer produced a grandchild clone shortly after it was assembled.

Couple that with the development of the EATR robot (see page 75), which extracts energy from the environment in the form of bio material that it converts to electricity, and you could be seeing such space-exploration technology in the not-too-distant future.

FACT

The Singularity Institute for Artificial Intelligence (SIAI) was founded in 2004 in the belief that in the coming decades, humanity will create a powerful artificial intelligence and to confront the opportunities and risks this presents.

The Turing test

In 1950, the British mathematician Alan Turing published a paper called "Computing machinery and intelligence." In it, he considered the question "can machines think?" and came up with what is now known as the Turing test. In the test, an interrogator asks questions of a human and a machine – who are isolated in a separate room – in a bid to discover which is which. A true artificial intelligence would pass the Turing test, something which has not yet been achieved.

Could Skynet become reality?

The ability for a network of computers to attain sentience is clearly a worry in a future world where more and more computers and other devices get connected together. As seen in Skynet from the series of *Terminator* movies, self-aware machines could prove extremely hazardous to the human race!

The network part of Skynet is already with us today, thanks to the Internet. The other element of Skynet, a self-aware artificial intelligence, is some way off. Humans can design a computer that has the appearance of intelligence, but they work according to instructions and sets of rules provided by human programmers that only gives the impression of intelligence.

LEFT Computer programs that can play chess already exist; could independent robots one day surpass human intelligence?

Cyborgs

The term cyborg, or cybernetic organism, was coined in 1960 in an article called Cyborgs and Space by scientists Manfred Clynes and Nathan Kline. The idea was that humans would fare better in the harsh environment of space by improving their bodies with artificial means rather than trying to recreate an Earth-like environment to live in.

The mad professor

The idea captured the imagination of both scientists and science-fiction writers. One scientist who has taken the cyborg idea further than most is Professor Kevin Warwick of the Department of Cybernetics at the University of Reading in England, who used a silicon chip implanted under his skin to operate doors, lights, heating, and computers without using his hands. A second device, implanted in 2002, was used to used to control a robotic hand and operate a motorized wheelchair.

Cyborg patients

Meanwhile, Stuart Harshbarger, a biomedical engineer at Johns Hopkins University, in England, is part of a team that has been working on targeted muscle reinnervation – a technique that allows people with prosthetic limbs to control them using signals from other muscles in their body, such as those in the chest. The technique has already been used successfully on patients.

Researchers at the University of Utah are working on a tiny brain implant that consists of 100 fine needles in an array that might be used to control a bionic arm but also feed back information from the arm to the brain. The team say real-life use of such devices is still "some years away."

Top three cyborgs on screen

1. **The Terminator:** *Arnold Schwarzenegger's cyborg in the multi-movie franchise is arguably the greatest outing on screen for these human/robot cocktails. Arnie successfully blends extreme violence and witty one-liners in a plot that twists and turns through time, backed up by a thumping rock soundtrack provided by Guns'n'Roses.*

2. **Robocop:** *In a not-too-distant future, the city of Detroit has succumbed to violent crime and faces financial ruin. In a bid to turn the city around, a huge conglomerate, Omni Consumer Products, is brought in to run it. Detroit's police force is privatized and law enforcement robots brought in to administer justice. OCP uses the body of a recently murdered police officer to create the world's first RoboCop. The near indestructible cyborg is programmed with three directives (in a nod to Isaac Asimov's three laws of robotics) – serve the public, trust and protect the innocent, and uphold the law.*

3. **Six Million Dollar Man:** *No one who grew up in the 1970s will ever forget the opening sequence of this TV series starring Lee Majors as Steve Austin. The spaceship bursts into flames and the voiceover says "We can rebuild him. We have the technology." Kids everywhere dreamed of having a bionic eye and the ability to jump tall buildings, filling playgrounds with the relevant sound effects.*

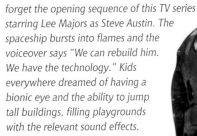

RIGHT The killer cyborg, *Terminator*.

WEIRD
WEAPONS AND
WARFARE

Techy troops

There have been some massive advancements in technological warfare over the past century. The human race has gone from carrying rifles and bayonets to deploying machine-gun-wielding semi-autonomous robots, and from wood and paper bi-planes of old to supersonic jets capable of striking targets hundreds of miles away. So what does the future hold for the battlefields of the world?

Future soldiers

The Future Soldier program is an umbrella name covering a range of projects by NATO members around the world, including Britain's FIST (Future Integrated Soldier Technology) project and America's Future Force Warrior (FFW) program. Future soldiers will be unlike those of today – they will rely on technology more than ever before, be networked with others on and off the battlefield, and enjoy even greater protection against enemy fire.

Extreme equipment

FIST incorporates more than 11,000 separate items including thermal sights for weapons, underslung grenade launchers, fire control systems, ruggedized digital cameras, and target-locating systems.

The FFW project, meanwhile, is looking at even more futuristic concepts. One of these is the idea of bulletproof panels that contain a fluid of metallic particles. When a current is applied, the fluid would solidify in an instant, making it impenetrable to bullets.

The US military's Natick Labs research center has been working on a helmet as part of the FFW program that includes a dropdown eyepiece display providing the soldiers with maps, soldier and enemy positions, targets, mission plans, and memory joggers.

Battle 'bots

Robots are already deployed on the battlefield, although they are always under the control of people, at least partially.

Semi-automotons

In 2009, the US Office of Naval Research issued a report on the ethics of autonomous military robots. It estimated that 5,000 semi-autonomous robots had already been used on the battlefield in Afghanistan and Iraq, such as drones (including aircraft), which can be autonomously guided to a target. However, it is always the decision of a human operator to open fire once there. Some believes that fully autonomous battlefield robots are just around the corner – ones that can locate enemies and engage them independently.

Man-eating robot?

One robot that is a step in this direction is the Energetically Autonomous Tactical Robot (EATR), which can travel long distances by "eating" biomass from its environment and converting it into energy. The company behind the robot, Ribotic Technology Inc, had to issue a statement last year saying the robot was strictly vegetarian, converting twigs, grass clippings, and wood chips into energy, after scare reports that it would consume dead bodies as it traveled around.

RIGHT Robots could become a much more regular feature on future battlefields, alongside regular troops.

Unmanned military vehicles

Unmanned military vehicles, whether on the ground, in the air, or under the water, offer the obvious advantage of not putting human operators at risk. The US military has a roadmap showing how unmanned military vehicles are likely to develop over the next 25 years. The report outlines

Operations	Project	Use	Program start date
Air	Floating Mine Neutralization Unmanned Aircraft System (UAS)	Launched from a ship, these would be used to destroy floating mines in the area.	2018
Air	Air Refueling UAS	These could be used to refuel aircraft while still in flight.	2020
Air	High Speed UAS	An attack drone that can reach any location worldwide within 2 hours.	2026
Air	Airborne telesurgery	An unmanned airborne surgical vehicle controlled by remote surgeons.	2034
Ground	Tunnel renaissance unmanned ground vehicle (UGV)	A vehicle capable of exploring tunnel and underground complexes.	2014
Ground	Small armed UGV advanced	An all weather, all terrain armed vehicle.	2017

existing technology and gives directions where research
might go in the future.

Some of the more futuristic military drones that are
planned are shown below. It is clear that military chiefs
want the ability to wage a war entirely from the comfort of
their bunkers.

Operations	Project	Use	Program start date
Ground	Crowd Control System	A robot for urban patrol and crowd control.	2017
Ground	Automated munitions handling/loading	A robot for arming aircraft.	2020
Sea	Amphibious UGV/unmanned sea vehicle (USV)	An unmanned vehicle capable of operation on land and at sea.	2014
Sea	Autonomous Undersea Mine Neutralization	A ship-launched unmanned submarine for destroying underwater mines.	2016
Sea	Harbor Security USV	An unmanned vehicle for patrolling harbors and engaging with unknown vessels with non-lethal weapons.	2016

Weapons of tomorrow

New weaponry is constantly in development Some of the weapons we see as futuristic may be with us in a surprisingly short time, while others remain firmly in the realm of science fiction.

New research for tanks

Each new generation of tanks lasts many years because of the high costs of developing new technologies. However, the use of tanks in new environments for which they were not originally designed does force innovation.

Areas of research for tanks include stealth technologies, like those used in aircraft, to make vehicles virtually invisible on the battlefield, and better armor to protect them from rocket-propelled grenades and armor-piercing shells. Interestingly, tanks may also start using hybrid engines to reduce their reliance on diesel, which requires extended supply chains, putting more troops in the line of fire.

Russia's T95, currently in development, looks set to be one of the most lethal tanks in the future. It is thought to be fitted with a 135 mm or 152 mm main gun and use an advance fire control system based on thermal and infrared imaging and possibly radar. It is thought to have a lower battlefield profile than existing tanks, making it harder to spot, and incorporate an armored capsule to house the crew, helping them survive in the event of missile attack.

Uncle Sam's next idea

America's future tanks are likely to come in two types. The US Army is already looking at an upgrade called the M1A3, which is expected to be a lighter-weight version of the M1A2 and may enter service by 2017. Others expect even lighter tanks, developed as part of the US Future Combat System, to take a greater role on the battlefield.

Smart bombs and brainy bullets

Current generation smart bombs use the same technology as in-car satellite navigation systems to find their targets. Joint Direct Attack Munition (JDAM) smart bombs are just dumb bombs (old bombs without guidance) with a smart tail attached, incorporating a GPS receiver and guidance fins.

The problem with JDAM

One of the problems with JDAM and other smart bomb technologies is accuracy. JDAM's accuracy is between 32 and 43 ft (10–13 m), which can make all the difference between a hit and a miss. Future smart bombs are likely to focus on improving this accuracy. With greater accuracy, next generation smart bombs will be smaller, causing less collateral damage.

Shooting around corners

It isn't only in bombs that the military is using smart technology. The XM25 rifle shows another smart technology at work.

Imagine you are a solder trying to shoot someone hidden in a gulley; you can only fire when they come into the line of sight. The XM25 prototype uses munitions that shatter into mini-grenades at a pre-determined range, allowing you to take out the enemy despite their being hidden.

FACT

In the realm of precision-guided weapons, there is a difference between a guided bomb and a guided missile; a bomb relies on the speed and height of the launch aircraft for propulsion, but a missile has an onboard engine to direct its flight.

The weapons of James Bond villains – reality or future?

The James Bond films have never been short of providing us with a few fun gadgets. Some of the weapons envisaged are based on reality, others are a little more futuristic.

Villain	Weapon	Reality or future
Alec Trevelyan, *GoldenEye*	Space-based nuclear weapon	**Future.** Space-based nuclear weapons are banned under the Outer Space Treaty, although not all countries are signatories.
Auric Goldfinger, *Goldfinger*	Laser beam	**Reality.** The most powerful laser in the world has a power of around a petawatt. You only need a couple of kilowatts to cut steel.
Ernst Stavro Blofeld, *You Only Live Twice*	Nuclear missiles launched from inside a volcano	**Future.** While nuclear missiles that can reach space have been around for decades, building a base inside a volcano is still a fantasy.
Gustav Graves, *Die Another Day*	Icarus satellite, using diamonds to concentrate sunlight	**Future.** Satellites deployed in geostationary orbits could concentrate solar power and beam it to Earth by 2016.
Oddjob, *Goldfinger*	Steel-brimmed derby hat	**Future.** Lack of demand rather than technical implausibility is the reason for its non-appearance.
Hugo Drax, *Moonraker*	Globes of nerve gas design to kill most of the world's population	**Reality.** Botulinum toxin (Botox) has already been created in population-killing quantities, although perhaps not from a space station.

Ray guns

Lasers appear to be the best hope of creating ray guns, a favorite sci-fi energy weapon, but there are a number of problems:

1. **High power requirements:** *Creating a handheld laser with enough power to kill or stun is currently in the realm of fiction.*

2. **Blooming:** *Laser beams tend to ionize the air, causing the beam to defocus and lose energy.*

3. **Absorption:** *Laser beams can easily be absorbed by dust or fog and can be reflected, unlike conventional projectiles.*

Ray guns in reality

The US army's Armament Research, Development, and Engineering Center (ARDEC) in New Jersey is working on a weapon called the Multimode Directed Energy Armament System (MDEAS), probably the closest to the sci-fi idea of a ray gun. The MDEAS uses a laser to create a path through the air and then sends a beam of microwaves along this channel to disable or destroy the target.

Non-lethal lasers

Weapons company Raytheon has also developed a non-lethal weapon called Silent Guardian. It projects a beam of millimeter waves, which causes burning sensations on the skin of people standing within its reach. Such systems have potential in repelling pirates from ships which have the devices mounted on their decks.

RIGHT In ray guns of science fiction, a beam transfers energy from the gun to a target by some unspecified means.

The lightsaber

It is the weapon we all wanted as children and some secretly still do! But will lightsabers ever become a reality?

How could it work?

If military researchers are looking at developing a real-life lightsaber, they might choose to avoid the obvious avenue of using laser technology. This has numerous problems, not least how to stop the beam a few feet from the handle and how you would make the beam hard (see below). Instead, they might want to look at a magnetically-confined plasma. Plasmas have unusual properties, including the ability to exclude electromagnetic fields, which could be used to give the impression of hardness.

Can light ever be hard?

James Clerk Maxwell, the Scottish physicist who developed the theory of electromagnetism, illustrated how electromagnetic radiation, including light, could exert a pressure. However, the pressure is so small that it is difficult to imagine how this could translate into "hard light."

RIGHT The *Star Wars* lightsaber is any sci-fi fan's most sought after weapon.

Sci-fi's best weapons

Science-fiction films are where people really have the chance to stretch their imaginations and come up with all sorts of weird and wonderful weapons that we might one day have. Not all of them are based on actual scientific developments and possibilities, in fact most of them probably aren't, but you never know what the future might hold. Here is a selection of a few of them.

Where	What	How
Against a Dark Background	Lazy gun	Different effects depending on target. People shot with it might be electrocuted or be savaged by an animal; vehicles might implode or disappear.
Hitchhiker's Guide to the Galaxy	Point of View gun	People shot with it are converted to your point of view.
Star Trek	Photon torpedoes	A matter/antimatter torpedo capable of destroying spaceships, cities, and even planets.
Star Wars	Lightsaber	A sword-like weapon created from a beam of light which can vaporize your opponent.
The War of the Worlds	Heat ray	Creates a beam of light and heat for killing humans and destroying buildings.

The future and force fields

Force fields, invisible shields of energy that protect individuals and objects from damage by weapons, have been in the public consciousness since the 1920s when they first started appearing in science fiction, particularly the works of E. E. "Doc" Smith. Since then, force fields have become a sci-fi staple, appearing in everything from *Star Trek* to *Dune*, although the actual functions and abilities of the technology varies between imaginations.

The ozone idea

Scientists have looked at the Earth's protective shield – the bubble of plasma that stops us being fried by solar radiation – as a potential technology that could be harnessed to make more personalized force fields.

Plasma is known as the fourth state of matter after gas, liquid, and air. It indicates a state in which the electrons have been stripped off the atoms. This state of matter has unusual electromagnetic properties, allowing objects surrounded by plasmas to deflect electrically charged and magnetized objects.

Researchers at the University of Washington in Seattle and Britain's Rutherford Appleton Laboratory have both looked at how to create such plasma bubbles in the laboratory: the former using it to surround a spacecraft, which would protect it from radiation and other interstellar particles; the latter trying to design a test satellite which would orbit the Earth in a protective plasma bubble.

Cloaking devices

Invisibility cloaks crop up everywhere in the science fiction imagination, from *Star Trek* to *Harry Potter*, but they may not be as fictional as we once supposed.

The invisibility cloak

Researchers at Duke University in North Carolina and Imperial College in London have demonstrated what they are calling the "first practical realization of an invisibility cloak." The teams used what are known as meta-materials: materials that have been designed to have unusual optical properties, bending light and other electromagnetic radiation in different ways than normal.

How it works

The teams created a copper cylinder that bent microwave radiation around it, effectively rendering it invisible to microwaves.

Meanwhile, a team including Graeme Milton of the University of Utah has produced a working mathematical model for a cloaking system that could use a technique called anomalous resonance, similar to the concept used by noise-canceling headphones. The problem is that it is hard to make something work for all frequencies of light, something that a practical invisibility cloak would need to do to be effective. That will prove more of a challenge.

Antimatter technology

The positron, the first known antimatter particle, was observed in 1932 at Caltech by Carl Anderson. Particle physicists now say that every fundamental particle has its own antimatter counterpart – the proton has its anti-proton and so on. But can it be used as a weapon?

The science bit

In fictional antimatter weapons, such as *Star Trek*'s photo torpedo, matter and antimatter annihilate each other to produce energy, with the amount created given by Einstein's famous equation $E = mc^2$. However, even though c (the speed of light) is very large, the mass of an electron is very small and the energy available from such annihilations is very limited. To make a useful antimatter bomb, you would need a substantial amount of antimatter.

FACT
Although there appears to be far less antimatter in the universe than matter, it is all around us. Our own bodies emit hundreds of positrons every minute through the radioactive decay of a chemical element called potassium-40.

Man-made antimatter

The particle physics laboratory CERN in Geneva makes antimatter using its accelerators. However, the amount it has made in its whole lifespan is less than 10 nanograms. If it annihilated with the same amount of matter, it would create only enough energy to power a 60W light bulb for four hours.

Biological and chemical warfare

The Biological and Toxin Weapons Convention, established in 1972, aims to prohibit the development, production, and stockpiling of chemical and biological weapons. By 2005, 171 countries had signed the convention. However, despite the ban, research into biological agents continues.

In the US, the National Biodefense Analysis and Countermeasures Center – part of the Department of Homeland Security – claims to study biological threats and seek ways of countering them. However, some scientists believe that its work is in breach of the Convention.

Rogue states and bio-warfare

Rogue states and non-state organizations are perhaps the biggest worry in terms of the development of biological weapons. Iraq, for example, produced hundreds of gallons of the botulinum toxin in the 1980s, enough to kill most of the world's population.

Despite the Convention, research into biological weapons clearly continues. One area of potential interest for the future might be the development of bio-agents that are targeted at specific individuals, using their DNA as a key.

Chemical crowd control

As with biological weapons, the existence of a Convention does not mean that all research into types of chemical weaponry has stopped, especially into those used to control crowds. Tear gas is still regularly used, while fentanyl gas was used in Moscow to end the 2002 theater siege, which saw the deaths of a large number of the hostages.

In 2007, Penn State University was awarded $250,000 into what it called "operationalizing calmatives," a neat grammatical way of side-stepping and avoiding the ban on chemical agents.

Future terrorism

Terrorists work by exploiting loopholes that expose their enemies to danger. The incidents of 9/11 show how terrorists were able to use lax airport security to hijack airliners and carry out their infamous attack.

So how will future terrorists operate?

Inevitably, as aviation security tightens up, terrorists look at places that are less well-protected, for example train stations. The problem for those aiming to combat such attacks is that protecting train stations – where people expect to just walk up and travel – is a much harder proposition than protecting airports.

Tackling terrorists

Catching terrorists before they attack is the main approach. Experts believe that the trend of decentralization within terrorist organizations and networks will continue, so that it is harder to disrupt the links within the chain of command. Finding them before they strike may rely on a combination of measures, including covert surveillance of public places and behavior modeling.

FACT

Terrorists have been quick to use new technologies, and adapt existing ones to their uses. They have exploited disposable cellular phones, over the counter long-distance calling cards, Internet cafes, and other means of anonymous communications. Embedding information in digital pictures and graphics is another innovation employed to enable the clandestine global communication that modern terrorists require.

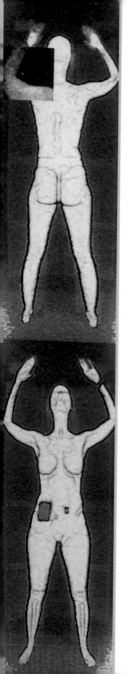

Future airport security

The 9/11 attacks and other aviation-related incidents such as the shoe bomber and the liquid bomb threat have all led to calls for greater security measures at airports, some of which have already been put in place.

The most recent addition to the range of devices at airports is the full body scanner, which has caused controversy because of the naked images it produces.

One current area of development for scanners is the use of T-rays rather than X-rays. T-rays are rays of terahertz frequency radiation, which give greater resolution than X radiation and at lower energies. One advantage of T-rays is that they penetrate clothing but not liquids.

Another innovative idea is proposed by Israel's WeCU Technologies. It suggests projecting images onto a wall and then monitoring the passenger's response to them. The company believes it can use the system to detect whether the passenger has the intent to carry out a terrorist attack.

LEFT Images created by a "backscatter" scanner, which can detect hidden metallic and nonmetallic objects without physical contact.

Space war

The launch of the Strategic Defense Initiative (SDI) in 1983 by US president Ronald Reagan saw the escalation of the Cold War into the reaches of space.

The real Star Wars

SDI was a plan to intercept and destroy strategic ballistic missiles before they reached US soil or that of its allies, using a combination of ground- and space-based technologies. As a result, SDI quickly became known as Star Wars.

The technologies ranged from the use of satellite-mounted X-ray and chemical lasers to high-velocity rail guns.

The spin-offs

Although the SDI program has been watered down and renamed many times since its conception, many of the technologies have enjoyed either direct success or valuable spin-offs.

For example, the chemical laser program has led to the development of the Boeing YAL-1 Airborne Laser system, which includes a chemical oxygen iodine laser inside a modified Boeing 747. In January 2010, the system successfully acquired, tracked, and engaged a missile target in the boost phase, although the trial was not designed to test its ability to destroy the target.

X-ray laser research, meanwhile, has led to developments in medical imaging in addition to their military uses.

THE FINAL FRONTIER

To infinity and beyond!

Most of what we know about the Universe has come from studies made on Earth. Humans haven't even made it past the Moon's orbit, but perhaps the future will be filled with space travel.

Space tourism

Burt Rutan's success in winning the $10 million Ansari X prize for the first successful, reusable non-commercial spacecraft with SpaceShipOne could lead to the first space holidays.

ABOVE
SpaceShipOne.

Rutan's technology is now the basis for Sir Richard Branson's Virgin Galactic's plans for trips to space. Under Branson's plans, tourists paying $200,000 a time will fly to 50,000 ft (15,000 m) in a specially designed "mothership" before transferring to the VSS (Virgin Space Ship) *Enterprise* – unveiled to the world in the Mojave Desert in December 2009.

Once safely on board, the *Enterprise*'s rockets will ignite, sending it climbing to higher than 68 miles (110 km) in just 90 seconds. After it reaches its highest point – at which the passengers (sorry, astronauts) will experience zero gravity – its wings will fold away and begin its descent back toward earth. At 60,000 ft (18,000 m), the wings are unfolded and the spaceship glides safely back down to the spaceport.

Travel to the moon

Another company, Space Adventures, is offering seats on the first private trip to the moon at a cost of $100 million apiece. The lucky – and wealthy – passenger will take off in a Soyuz rocket, rendezvousing with a booster in low Earth orbit. The combined vehicle will then have enough fuel to get to the far side of the Moon and back.

Top five solar system sights to see before you die

1. **Martian skiing:** *The highest mountain in the Solar System is Olympus Mons, a dormant volcano found on Mars. At 16 miles (27 km) high, it is three times higher than Everest and measures 342 miles (550 km) around the base. What snow there is will be made of carbon dioxide rather than water, while the low gravity will make the jumps spectacular.*

2. **Cruising the Lake District...on Titan:** *The Cassini mission to Saturn has made a number of discoveries, including that of one or more huge lakes on the surface of the planet's largest moon, Titan. One day, we might see Cunard's Queen Elizabeth IV cruise ship plying Titan's liquid hydrocarbon lakes.*

3. **Mars' Grand Canyon:** *If you thought Arizona's Grand Canyon was impressive, what about Valles Marineris? This Martian gorge system is 2,500 miles (4,000 km) long, tens to hundreds of miles wide, and up to 6 miles (10 km) deep: hundreds of Grand Canyons could fit inside it. Hiking down to the canyon floor will be the active holiday of the future.*

4. **Comet surfing:** *The world's space agencies has already smashed spacecraft into comets so it can't be long until they come up with a softer landing. Anyone for Halley's comet on its return later this century?*

5. **Saturn solar eclipse:** *Although the Earth is unusually blessed when it comes to eclipses – the Moon and Sun have an almost identical apparent size in the sky – they are not unique to our home planet. Future space holidaymakers might like to orbit Saturn to catch a solar eclipse there.*

FACT
The hottest surface in the Solar System (other than the surface of the Sun) is to be found on Venus, which has an average temperature of 842°F (450°C).

The problems of space tourism

Anyone wanting a holiday in space needs to take more than a bottle of sun cream and malaria tablets if they want to be safe. Here are some of the challenges:

Radiation: *Life on earth is protected from the solar wind and cosmic rays by the magnetosphere but there is little protection when you are in space. Astronauts on the International Space Station have to go into a specially protected room when solar activity is predicted to be high.*

Micrometeorites: *As well as the larger meteorites that cause shooting stars, the solar system is peppered with smaller particles traveling at high speeds that can easily penetrate the shell of a spacecraft or a space traveler's spacesuit.*

Muscle wasting: *Your muscles are finely tuned to the Earth's gravitational field. If you are traveling in deep space, the prolonged weightlessness causes muscle wastage. Spaceship designers will need to think about artificial gravity (through spinning) or other means to cope.*

Journey time: *The distances involved in getting anywhere interesting in space mean that we will have to work out how to travel much faster or think about suspended animation techniques, such as cryogenics, to relieve the boredom of long trips.*

Time dilation: *If we do work out how to achieve speeds that approach or exceed the speed of light, time dilation will mean that space travelers will age differently from those left at home.*

Terraforming

The word terraforming – rebooting another planet so that it
becomes habitable for the human race – was coined by sci-fi
writer Jack Williamson in the 1940s although the concept
has been around for longer.

What on earth is it?

Most terraforming experts see the introduction onto an
existing uninhabitable planet of microbes, which convert the
poisonous atmosphere into something more palatable for
humans and animals.

Just making the atmosphere breathable is not enough
though. Depending on the planet you terraform, you might
also need to alter the surface temperature in some way to
allow liquid water to exist – considered a prerequisite for
life. You may also need to tinker with the atmosphere to
ensure that anyone on the surface is not instantly fried by
cosmic rays or the solar wind.

Could it happen?

Terraforming is not just a dream. NASA's 2008 Astrobiology
Roadmap sets out how research and exploration might be
prioritized and coordinated. One of the goals set out in the
roadmap asks the question "What is the future of life on
Earth and beyond?"

Top five places for terraforming

If we are ever able to develop the technology to terraform a new planet, where would we be most likely to succeed and what obstacles would we have to overcome?

1. **Mars:** *Probably the most likely candidate for terraforming. The major challenges are Mars' thin carbon dioxide atmosphere and the low temperature.*

2. **Venus:** *The radius and mass of Venus make it very like Earth. However, a surface temperature of 842°F (450°C) and its superdense acidic atmosphere are the big barriers to terraforming.*

3. **Europa:** *Jupiter's moon is a tempting target thanks to the liquid water that astronomers suspect lurks there. We would need to work out how to survive being killed by radiation from Jupiter though.*

4. **Callisto:** *Another Jovian moon might be more appealing. Callisto has water ice and possibly even oxygen in its atmosphere. It also doesn't have the radiation problems of Europa.*

5. **The Moon:** *Don't hold a party on the Moon, the joke goes, there's just no atmosphere. Creating an atmosphere might be an easier option than converting an unsuitable existing one on a planet such as Mars.*

ABOVE Imagined stage-by-stage terraforming of Mars to make the planet habitable.

Goldilocks planets

Astronomers looking for places where alien life might exist in the universe are beginning to concentrate their efforts on what are known as Goldilocks planets – those that are not too cold and not too hot but are just right, like the fairy tale porridge.

Planet spotting

To find extrasolar planets – i.e. planets outside our solar system – researchers use techniques such as measuring the dimming of a star's light as a planet passes in front of it or how much a star wobbles relative to Earth due to the gravitational effect of the planet.

A planet far, far away...

In 2007, Swiss astronomers found a number of planets orbiting the red dwarf star Gliese 581, 20 light-years from Earth in the constellation Libra.

The planet Gliese 581 d looks the most promising. It is just on the edge of the habitable zone and, with a bit of warming from the greenhouse effect, the temperature may be right about right for the presence of liquid water.

FACT

In an attempt to communicate with potential alien civilizations, a radio signal was sent from the Arecibo telescope in Puerto Rico to a star cluster that lies 25,000 light years away. The earliest we are likely to receive a reply (if at all) will be in 50,000 years' time.

Where next for space exploration?

Would-be space explorers had some of their dreams shattered in February 2010 when US President Barack Obama cancelled plans put in place by his predecessor, George W Bush, for NASA to send astronauts back to the Moon by 2020. However, NASA chief Charles Bolden says that the agency still has human exploration of the solar system, and Mars in particular, as one of its goals. He admits that no manned mission will be possible in the next decade.

International space race

It is not just NASA with plans to send people back toward the stars. China has also entered the space race with its successful Shenzhou V mission and is already planning to go to the Moon, although there are no firm plans as yet.

Other nations are also in the race. India launched its Chandrayaan-1 moon mission in October 2008. It sent a spacecraft into orbit 62 miles (100km) above the surface of the moon and dropped a lander onto the surface. The Indian Space Research Organization is also looking to launch an unmanned mission to Mars in 2013–14 and its first manned mission to space in 2014–15.

Japan plans to build on the success of its Selene mission to the Moon with the launch of Selene-2 by the middle of this decade. This mission intends to place an unmanned rover on the lunar surface in order to learn more about our satellite's origin.

Space food

Space food has come a long way. John Glenn and the Mercury astronauts had to eat unappetizing cubes, freeze-dried powders, and semi-liquids stuffed in squeezable tubes.

Space voyages and use-by dates

With the Shuttle missions coming to an end, NASA's immediate focus is on the International Space Station and developing foods that are appetizing and nutritious for long-stay astronauts but also have extended shelf live.

Looking beyond that, NASA's Advanced Food Technology project, led by a team at the Johnson Space Center, is looking at developing foods that can be stored for three to five years. The team is also working on ways to reduce packaging waste and developing ways of planting and growing vegetable crops in space that minimize crew time, power, and water needs.

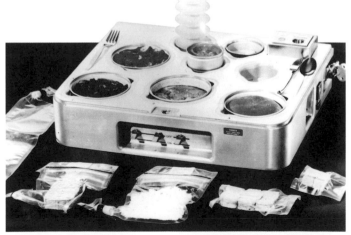

ABOVE Skylab food was a vast improvement on the food used in earlier space flights. In the future, we could see delicious three course meals during voyages.

Future spaceships

Current spacecraft technology is just not speedy enough for real exploration of the universe. The main problem is that current rockets need to take their chemical fuels with them. If you want to go anywhere significant – such as to another star – you need to find another way of getting there.

Ramjets and scramjets (see page 38) provide a possible answer, since the fuel required is gathered from the surroundings rather than needing to take it with you. A ramjet-powered spacecraft would take hydrogen (or rather protons) from the interstellar medium and generate energy from nuclear fusion. Some doubt this would work because of the energy required for fusion.

Plasma propulsion

Escaping Earth's gravitational tug means that conventional rockets have to carry enormous amounts of fuel just to get into orbit. Spacecraft that use the physical properties of plasma can get around this problem because they can produce high exhaust velocities.

Plasma thrusters have been widely used in Soviet space missions and were used on the European Space Agency's SMART-1 lunar orbiter mission in 2003.

NASA is hoping that a propulsion system called the Variable Specific Impulse Magnetoplasma Rocket (VASIMR) might be used for future interplanetary missons, particularly to Mars. VASIMR uses hydrogen as its fuel source – which means that a spacecraft could pick up fuel wherever it goes in the Solar System – and contains it as a plasma in a metal cylinder using magnetic fields. One of the tubes is deliberately made leaky, creating thrust.

ABOVE Solar sails powering a spacecraft.

Solar sails

One possible future propulsion
technology is the use of a solar
sail. Rather like the sail of a yacht that catches the wind on
Earth, a solar sail is nudged along by a combination of the
solar wind – the constant stream of particles emitted by the
Sun – and radiation pressure. It is this combination that
makes comet tails point away from the Sun.

Because this "wind" is not particularly strong, it is
proposed to use sail materials that are extremely thin and
light, typically aluminum foils that are micrometers thick.

Several missions have been launched to test aspects of
the technology, particularly looking at how to deploy the
fine sails quickly and without tearing them. Sadly, several
missions have failed due to problems with their rockets
(rather than with the sail). Nasa's NanoSail-D mission in
August 2008 failed two minutes after take-off after the
launch rocket failed to separate properly and it didn't reach
Earth's orbit. Testing a sail in space as a propulsion system is
still some way off.

Sci-fi's greatest spaceships

Most science fiction creations involve some kind of intergalactic craft. Here are a selection of the best.

Spaceship	Sci-fi source	Description
Borg cube	*Star Trek: The Next Generation*	An unaerodynamic shape for a spaceship but that just adds to its menace.
Destroyers	*Independence Day*	15 mile-wide saucers with lasers that can destroy buildings, famously including the White House.
Heart of Gold	*Hitchhiker's Guide to the Galaxy*	Infinite improbability drive, a quantum theory propulsion system that passes through every point in space at once with weird side effects.
Millennium Falcon	*Star Wars*	A modified freight spaceship with the ability to "make the Kessel Run in less than 12 parsecs."
Mothership	*Close Encounters of the Third Kind*	The scene of the ship hovering over Devil's Tower National Monument in this film is one of the most memorable in cinema history.

Space stations

The idea of the space station is nearly 40 years old. The Soviet Union launched Salyut in 1971, three years after the release of the film *2001: A Space Odyssey*. 2001 has now come and gone but the film's enormous balletic space station is still a pipe-dream.

The ISS

The International Space Station is a collaboration that grew out of the aborted race for building space stations at the end of the Cold War. The first element of the ISS was placed in orbit in 1998 and should be completed by the end of 2011. Over its 30-year-life,

ABOVE Space stations would allow more in-depth research in outer space.

the ISS is expected to cost 100 billion euros. A wide range of research will take place on board, including studies of the harmful effects of space flight on the human immune system and of how micro-organisms survive on board spacecraft.

Other orbital ideas

China also has plans for a space station, called *Tiangong*, or Heavenly Palace. An 8.5 tonne module is expected to be launched in the next year and act as a stepping stone for future Chinese manned space missions. The space station is expected to operate without crew for much of its life.

The space stations portrayed in *2001: A Space Odyssey* and *Star Trek* appear to be decades off. What may speed things up is the development of technologies that enable the construction of units in space.

Science of the Death Star

The Death Star from the *Star Wars* series of movies is perhaps the ultimate weapon from the science-fiction canon – a small moon-sized laser beam capable of destroying entire planets.

Could we make it?

Star Wars aficionados have used the size of the main characters and their scale compared to the Millennium Falcon to estimate the diameter of the Death Star as around 80 miles (130 km).

A Canadian writer called Ryszard Gold came up with an estimate of $15.6 septillion for building and launching a Death Star, based on the cost of steel and the cost of NASA launching a tonne of material. According to Gold, this incredible sum is a trillion times the total amount of money in the world.

Lethal lasers

Meanwhile, the website stardestroyer.net estimates that the energy required to destroy an entire planet is of the order of 2×10^{32} joules. The world's most powerful laser – the National Ignition Facility at the Lawrence Livermore National Laboratory – can only generate 4 million joules, a tiny fraction of that required to destroy a planet.

If someone did manage to build a Death Star, you would really want to make sure that it couldn't be destroyed by a single proton torpedo, though.

ABOVE The Death Star and TIE fighters from the *Star Wars* films.

Future spacecraft missions

Man's quest to explore the heavens looks set to continue for many decades yet. Space agencies around the world have big ideas, but what can we expect to see over the next few years?

Mission	When	What
Glory (NASA)	2010	Study of aerosols and black carbon in the Earth's atmosphere.
Juno (NASA)	2011	33 orbits around Jupiter's polar regions to study the planet's origins and atmosphere.
Mars Science Laboratory (NASA)	2011	Mars rover mission to see if there was ever microbial life on the planet.
Global Precipitation Measurement (JAXA/NASA)	2013	To measure rain and snowfall around the globe using a combination of satellites.
BepiColombo (ESA/JAXA)	2014	Eight year mission to study the planet Mercury.
ExoMars (ESA)	2016	Mars orbiter, descent vehicle, and rover to lay a path for future Mars exploration.
Venera-D (Russia)	2016	Venus probe to prospect future landing sites.
Celesta (Russia)	2018	Star mapping mission.
Terion (Russia)	2018	Geophysics mission.
Lisa (ESA)	2020 (approx.)	To study gravitational waves from black holes and other massive objects in the universe.
Solar Orbiter (ESA)	2020 (approx.)	To produce images of the sun at an unprecedented resolution and perform closest ever in-situ measurements.

Your guide to first contact

The SETI (Search for Extraterrestrial Intelligence) Institute has put together a handy nine-point declaration of principles if a signal is discovered. The points are as follows:

1. *Make sure the signal really is alien rather than a natural phenomenon or human. It'll be embarrassing for all involved if that muffled alien message turns out to be your neighbor singing in the shower.*

2. *Inform the SETI Institute and other research organizations that have signed the declaration of the discovery to seek independent confirmation.*

3. *Inform the International Astronomical Union, the Secretary General of the United Nations, the International Telecommunication Union, and a number of other international bodies.*

4. *Inform the public through scientific channels and public media. Make sure you have your legally binding declaration of discovery signed by the UN and SETI to hand in case people think you are another crackpot.*

5. *Make data available to the international scientific community as they are considerably smarter than you.*

6. *Data bearing on the evidence of extraterrestrial intelligence should be recorded and stored permanently to the greatest extent feasible and practical. If in doubt, ask your new friends at the UN if they can help. In general, they are a helpful bunch.*

7. *If the evidence of detection is in electromagnetic signals, seek protection of those frequencies from interference – people will hack anything.*

8. *No response to a signal should be sent until appropriate international consultations have taken place. Starting an intergalatic war could be just a click away.*

9. *An international committee of scientists and other experts should be established to serve as a focal point for continuing analysis of all evidence. They will be there to take over and steal all your glory.*

SETI's next step

Much of the search for extraterrestrial intelligence is now piggybacking on other astronomy projects to make best use of valuable time on telescopes.

For example, the SERENDIP (Search for Extraterrestrial Radio Emissions from Nearby Developed Intelligent Populations) project at UC Berkeley uses the Arecibo L-band Feed Array (ALFA) on the Arecibo radio telescope in Puerto Rico to scan for evidence of alien radio signals.

A window into new worlds

One of its biggest hopes for finding alien life in the future is the Allen Telescope Array (ATA), named after Microsoft's Paul Allen, who donated much of the money required to build it. ATA works using an array including a large number of small radio telescopes linked together using a technique known as interferometry. At present, the array includes 42 dishes but there are plans to increase this to 300, when funding permits. It is currently being used to conduct all-sky surveys in a wide range of frequencies (from 500 MHz to 11.2 GHz) for both traditional radio astronomy and the search for alien life.

Seeing signals

Various teams around the world are also conducting SETI searches for optical signals, such as the visible light emitted by a powerful laser. Berkeley scientists are searching for both short pulses of laser and beams that remain on permanently – perhaps an alien civilization trying to contact us.

The Voyager disc

The two Voyager spacecraft have by now long left the solar system. However, there is a chance that an alien civilization may one day stumble across them.

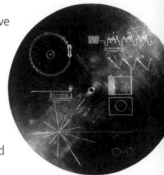

ABOVE The Voyager disc.

Intergalactic greetings

With this in mind, NASA placed a 12-inch gold-plated copper disc on board containing 115 images and a variety of natural sounds, a range of music from different cultures and eras, and spoken greetings in 55 languages. Each record is encased in a protective aluminum jacket, together with a cartridge and a needle. Instructions, in symbolic language, explain the origin of the spacecraft and indicate how the record is to be played. The disc also contains printed messages from US President Jimmy Carter and former UN Secretary General Kurt Waldheim, a map showing the location of Earth, and instructions on how to convert the analogue sounds on the disc into pictures.

Even if the discs are eventually found – and it will take thousands of years before they reach even the next nearest star – many doubt whether aliens will be able to decipher the information on them.

One problem is that we do not know what form alien life – if it exists – will take. Perhaps aliens will not have ears or perhaps they will be amorphous blobs that do not have the capacity to use the cartridge and needle. Indeed, they may be the size of planets and not even notice the spacecraft crashing into their vast bodies like some intergalactic fly.

THE WORLD IN 2050

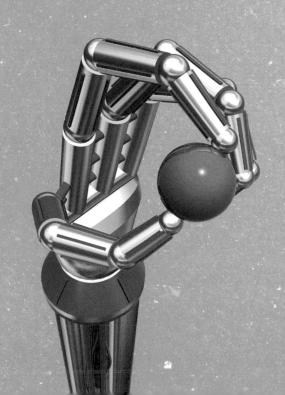

Future predictions

There are plenty of predictions for the future; some are based on fact and could become reality, while others are just based on wild imagination. Only the future knows which is which...

What futurologists say about 2050

Futurist Richard Watson creates amazing maps that show timelines to the future. Here are some predictions for 2050:
- First child born in space
- People able to record every event form birth to death
- Cosmetic brain surgery
- First Moon mine
- Self-repairing roads
- Digital cash widely embedded in human body
- First Internet courts
- Baby licenses
- 75 year mortgages
- Artificial livers

Nanotechnology expert Brian Wang has his own thoughts:
- Offworld economies, accounting for more than 100 million people, will be larger than Japan's
- *Star Trek*-style holodecks become reality
- Organ replacement with nanotechnology
- Interstellar probe reaches another solar system
- Real-time thought scanning
- Faster-than-light travel
- Artificial intelligence a billion times more clever than a human speeds up technology development
- Two-hour global package delivery service
- Physical currency eliminated
- Half a billion people killed in a nanotechnology-weapon war

Changing climates

The UN's Intergovernmental Panel on Climate Change (IPCC) released its fourth assessment report in 2007. It makes a number of predictions for what will happen to the Earth's climate over the next 90 years. While there is much controversy surrounding the work of the IPCC, it represents the crystalized wisdom of the vast majority of the world's scientists.

Global warming

The report suggests that, depending on which scenario of greenhouse gas emissions you choose, mean global temperatures will rise by between 34.3 and 35.2°F (1.3 and 1.8°C) by the middle of this century.

Rising seas

The panel also predicts that sea levels will rise on average by between 2 and 6 inches (5 and 15 cm) due to thermal expansion of the water in the Earth's oceans by 2050.

Over the next 40 years, precipitation events – i.e. rainstorms – will become more intense, particularly in tropical and high latitude areas that experience increases in mean precipitation. For subtropical and mid-latitude regions, where average rainfall is set to fall over the period, the intensity of rainfall will also be higher but it will rain less frequently.

Water shortages

Some experts predict that 75 percent of the population will face water shortages by 2050, due to a combination of the growing global population, climate change, and an increasing scarcity of fresh water. This could lead to an increasing number of conflicts over water, with the Middle East likely to be the most common battleground thanks to its relative lack of access to fresh water compared to its population.

Salty solution

Looking ahead, the world will have to find other ways of finding fresh water. The most promising is desalination, which is already in widespread use, particularly in the Middle East. This process covers a number of technologies, such as reverse osmosis and solar desalination, which converts seawater into fresh water. However desalination has its problems – it has high costs, requires the use of large amounts of energy, and produces problematic waste.

Hydro-hydration

Another potential source of water is hydrogen fuel cells. These combine hydrogen and oxygen to create electricity, heat, and water. NASA uses fuel cells in its manned space vehicles to provide power as well as water for the crew.

FACT

Water shortages could also create social challenges. A 2009 report predicted that without water productivity gains South Asia would need 57 percent more water for irrigated agriculture and East Asia 70 percent more. Asia as a whole could face the prospect of having to import 25 percent of its rice, wheat, and maize requirements.

When fossil fuels run out

The US Geological Survey currently estimates that the total amount of oil that has and will ultimately be recovered is around three trillion barrels. Forecasters have made many estimates of this figure over time and it generally increases mainly due to better geological, geophysical, and reservoir engineering information.

Oil peak

The big concern for the world is what is known as peak oil, the moment when the maximum rate of oil extraction is reached and starts declining. Some predict we may already have reached it. However, the US Energy Information Administration (EIA) has put the date of peak oil at somewhere between 2021 and 2112 . If we manage to curb our appetite for oil or there are substantial undiscovered reserves we may be able to put off the arrival of peak oil.

Coal store

The EIA also estimates that there are 930 billion tons of coal reserves around the world. At current rates of consumption, that would last for 138 years. However, consumption is actually increasing and the world's population is increasing so we may run out long before that.

Gas guzzling

As for natural gas, it is estimated that worldwide reserves total 6.254 quadrillion cubic ft (0.18 quadrillion cubic m). Gas consumption is currently increasing at around 1.6 percent per year, which means we will run out in around 63 years.

Has evolution stopped?

Scientists are divided on whether human evolution has stopped. Some believe that advances in technology mean that natural selection through genes is no longer important.

The evolution divide

Steve Jones, a geneticist at University College London, argues that natural selection has effectively stopped in humans because, due to advances in human medicine, children are now almost certain to reach reproductive age, and thus pass on their genes to the next generation.

However, research published in the New England Journal of Medicine in 2009 appeared to show that human evolution continues. Scientists at the UK's Medical Research Council showed that a community in Papua New Guinea which had suffered a major epidemic of a fatal brain disease called *kuru*, similar to CJD, had developed strong genetic resistance to the disease in a short timescale.

Big brains

Technology has also been seen to influence human evolution. There has long been a conundrum relating to why human brains have grown bigger over time, despite their ravenous appetite for energy. Some argue that the development of stone tools enabled humans to hunt energy-rich meat from animals and cultivate better crops, allowing the brain to grow larger.

This means that the technologies we are using today may influence the course of human evolution in the future.

What will we be recycling in 2050?

Humans produce a vast amount of waste, and current recycling habits will have to be improved in the future:

- *Figures from the US Environmental Protection Agency show that Americans recycled 33.2 percent of their waste in 2008, increased from 10.1 percent in 1985 and 26 percent in 1995.*

- *Latest figures from Australia show that 52 percent of waste was recycled, but there is a dramatic difference between the country's states – around a third in Western Australia and three quarters in Australian Capital Territory.*

- *The EU introduced a waste directive which means that by 2020 European countries will have to reduce the amount of biodegradable waste that currently goes to landfill to 35 percent of what it was in 1995.*

Zero waste nations

Many countries are looking at becoming zero waste nations by 2050, where no biodegradable waste goes to landfill. Waste incinerators may be the way forward, but they have the disadvantage of creating pollutants and emitting high levels of carbon dioxide.

Techno-garbage

One of the big challenges for future recycling concerns electronic devices. Every time you get a new mobile phone, for example, what happens to your old one?

Modern electronic devices often contain rare and difficult to recycle materials. Various countries and regions have introduced legislation to force manufacturers to take back unwanted devices. By 2050, you might find iPod recycling bins alongside those for bottles and newspapers.

The last 40 years vs the next 40 years

Eighty years is a long time. What changes have we seen over the last 40 years and what could we see in the next?

Year	What happened
1970	String theory, liquid crystal displays, Boeing 747 maiden flight, first successful landing on Venus, Concorde's first supersonic flight.
1975	Altair 8800 microcomputer goes on sale, Microsoft founded, Apollo and Soyuz spacecraft dock in orbit for the first time.
1980	Pac-Man arcade game released, CNN 24 hour news goes on air, camcorder patented.
1985	Windows released, Sinclair C5 electric vehicle launched, ozone hole discovered, discovery of buckminsterfullerene.
1990	World Wide Web, Launch of Hubble Space Telescope, first GPS sat navs for cars.
1995	Javascript introduced, DVDs launched, start of eBay and Amazon websites.
2000	International Space Station gets first permanent crew, billionth person born in India.
2005	YouTube launched, Philips iCat, Xbox 360 released.
2010	Burj Khalifa (world's tallest building) opens, Avatar opens at the box office, Apple iPad launched.

Year	What will happen
2015	Most software written by machine, gene therapy to combat hair loss, retirement age raised to 75, superconductivity at room temperature.
2020	Genetically modified robots, smart bacteria weapons, fuel cells replace internal combustion engines, life expectancy reaches 100.
2025	Android gladiators, full direct brain links, global voting, 3D home printers.
2030	Teaching replaced by interface to learning computers, artificial nerves, nanotech war.
2035	Space elevator, regular manned missions to Mars, experience recording, creation of The Matrix.
2040	Runaway global warming, start of construction of manned Mars lab, asteroid used as weapon, artificial brain.
2045	Artificial precipitation induction and control, nuclear fusion as power source, world population peaks at 10 billion.
2050	Ozone hole disappears.

Source: Future predictions from the BT Technology Timeline.

Changing superpowers

A superpower is generally a country or group of countries that has the ability to influence events around the world, usually through a combination of financial muscle and military superiority.

Superpowers of the past

The number of superpowers has changed in the past and will continue to change. Before the Second World War, the US, Soviet Union, and the British Empire could be considered as the world's superpowers. The granting of independence to many countries and the creation of the British Commonwealth reduced that to two. The end of the Cold War and the dissolution of the Soviet Union probably means there is now only one. However, the European Union may well be classified as a superpower in the future due to its growing cohesion and size.

Superpowers of the future

It also pays to look at population and economic forecasts to see where other superpowers might arise. In chapter 1, we read how the United Nations forecasts that the world's population will be somewhere between 7.9 and 11 billion by 2050, depending on whether you take an optimistic or pessimistic view.

Consultants PricewaterhouseCoopers published a report called The World in 2050 in 2006 which looks at how the economies of the seven richest nations at present – the G7 club of the US, Japan, Germany, UK, France, Italy, and Canada – would compare with the seven largest emerging market economies, the E7 group of China, India, Brazil, Russia, Indonesia, Mexico, and Turkey. It predicts that the E7

Most populous countries 2009		Most populous countries 2050	
China	1,331 million	India	1,748 million
India	1,171 million	China	1,437 millon
United States	307 million	United States	439 million
Indonesia	243 million	Indonesia	343 million
Brazil	191 million	Pakistan	335 million

Source: Forecasts from Population Reference Bureau 2009 World Population Datasheet.

FACT
The United Nations forecasts that India's population will overtake that of China by 2050 and that their joint populations will account for over half of the total world population.

economies will be up to 75 percent larger than the combined G7 economies by the middle of the 21st and that India's economy will be around 60 percent of the US economy at 2050.

On that basis, coupled with the population predictions in the box (above), China and India could join the superpower club in the next few decades.

Minority Report: could this be the future?

The movie *Minority Report*, based on the short story by Philip K. Dick, is set in the year 2054. Director Stephen Spielberg assembled a group of futurologists to guide his vision of the world in 2054, so could his vision become reality?

Prediction	Now	2050
Crime prevention through the use of future-seeing "pre-cogs."	ESP, crystal ball gazing, and tarot reading have no scientific basis.	**Highly unlikely.** Even if predicting the future does turn out to be scientifically valid, the social issues surrounding its use will prevent its introduction in policing.
Jetpacks for police officers.	Jetpacks exist but have a maximum usable life of around 30 seconds.	**Highly likely.** Police could use jetpacks based on personal plasma thrusters or, possibly, by anti-gravitons.
3D holographic displays, zoomable and draggable by hand gestures.	3D movies and televisions are starting to appear.	**Certain.** The necessary technology should be with us by 2020 let alone 2050.
Maglev cars.	Maglev is already being used successfully in trains.	**Likely.** The biggest barrier to widespread use will be the infrastructure costs associated with adding superconducting magnets to the road network.
Personalized billboard advertising.	Oil company Castrol is using number plate recognition to create personalized billboard ads selling engine oil, and adverts could also be targeted at Bluetooth cell phones.	**Certain.** The technology is already with us and it won't be long before it's the norm rather than the exception.

ABOVE *Minority Report* was rife with futuristic technology that could become reality in 2050, including 3-D holographic displays, controlled by hand gestures.

Future of money

Many forward-looking people dream of a global, single currency. Some say that the US dollar is already a de facto global currency, since around two thirds of foreign reserves held by governments are in dollars and most commodities, such as oil and gold, are priced in dollars.

Electrocash

Whether we do end up with a single global currency (or universal if we discover alien life), the days of money itself – the physical coins and banknotes – could be numbered. Increasingly, transactions are handled electronically and people throughout the world are using cards, services like PayPal, and even mobile phones to pay for things. Some futurists predict that by 2050 we will have a smart chip embedded in our bodies, allowing you to wave a hand over a terminal in order to pay for something.

Health and medicine

What will health and medicine be like by 2050? In the paper "What will doctors be doing by 2050?", Samreen Rizvi makes a number of predictions:

- greater use of the Internet to allow patients to identify problems earlier
- use of stem cells to regenerate tissue and organs
- computer-based diagnosis of patients
- wider use of robotic surgeons
- widespread use of individual gene therapy

AIDS confined to history

Some scientists believe AIDS could be eradicated by 2050. Dr. Brian Williams of the South African Center for Epidemiological Modeling and Analysis says that the introduction of a worldwide screening program by 2015, coupled with the use of anti-retroviral drugs to treat those affected, could lead to the eradication of AIDS by 2050.

Alzheimer's epidemic

However, the incidence of other diseases will spiral. Researchers at Johns Hopkins Bloomberg School of Public Health predict that the number of people worldwide with Alzheimer's disease will quadruple to 106 million.

Causes of death

Our rich lifestyles will be killing us in greater numbers by 2050. WHO director general Dr. Margaret Chan says that a third of deaths will be caused by cardiovascular disease, cancer, and car crashes by the middle of the century, while tobacco would remain the single largest preventable killer.

Telesurgery

The first major telesurgery – the removal of a gall bladder –
took place in September 2001, with a surgeon in New York
controlling a robot arm in Strasbourg, France.

Remote surgery is not yet a widespread technology and
there are still issues that need to be resolved involving
protocols, training, equipment, and procedures to cope
with any disruptions in communication or technology
malfunctions. But the technology does exists today, meaning
in the future expert medical care could be available across
the globe, even in remote areas.

Life expectancies

As medical technology and treatments improve, life
expectancies will naturally increase globally:

Country	Life expectancy for those born in 2005–10	Life expectancy for those born in 2045–50
Australia	81.5	86.2
Canada	80.7	85.2
China	73.0	79.3
Japan	82.7	87.2
Swaziland	45.8	58.6
UK	79.4	84.1
USA	79.2	83.3
WORLD	67.6	75.5

Sources: UN World Population Prospects 2008.

The year 3000

If we compare the world of today with that of a millennium ago, it is clear that there have been immense changes. The average life expectancy was somewhere in the 30s, people tended to live where they were born and not move far from their birthplace. The plough had been invented centuries before but the printing press was still a distant dream. Anyone who lived then who could see what we have now, a thousand years later, would be convinced that it was all witchcraft. For people living today, looking ahead another thousand years is just as difficult. However, some have tried. Here are a few of the best:

- Global temperatures have risen to 46.4°F (8°C) above pre-industrial levels and sea levels have risen by more than 24 ft (7.3 m).

- Humans will reach their physical peak, have coffee-colored skin, measure an average 6 ft (1.8 m) tall and live for up to 120 years.

- Large families are consigned to an irresponsible history. People are allowed no more than two children to help maintain the world's population.

- A single global language will be spoken by a united planetary population.

- People will no longer have to work in offices as new holographic technologies make virtual meetings from home the norm. All manual labor is done by robots.

- After catastrophic food shortages during the previous millenia, artificial nutrients have long since replaced normal meals and farming is a thing of the past. Food is now produced in labs.

- Traffic jams, delays, and lost luggage are all a thing of the past as teleportation stations offer instantaneous travel anywhere in the world.

- The terraforming of Mars will be well underway as humans search for more living space as Earth will no longer be able to sustain our ever-growing population.

- Earth-like planets will be discovered in far away solar systems and mapped by amazingly powerful telescopes. Actually getting there will still present a problem.

- Spacecraft will be faster and more efficient than ever, utilizing new energy technologies and nano-robotics.

- There will be regular manned missions to Jupiter's moon Titan, as well as other moons in the solar system. Plans to put permanent bases on them, much like the centuries old Moonbase, are in full swing.

- The hunt for alien life will continue...

PICTURE CREDITS

The publishers would like to thank the following for permission to reproduce pictures.

Alamy: pp. 23, 48, 55, 72, 75, 83, 98, 121. Corbis: pp. 15, 57. Dreamstime: pp. 9, 12, 13, 21, 31, 34, 51, 63, 64, 66, 68, 84, 89, 109, 111, 113, 114, 115, 118, 122, 124. Getty Images: p. 89. iStock photo: pp. 7, 8, 16, 17, 20, 30, 36, 40, 42, 70, 73, 94, 100, 103. NASA: pp. 38, 96, 97, 107, 108. Rex Features: pp. 32, 37. Science Photo Library: p. 24. US Navy: p. 52. Virgin Galactic: p. 92.